T0352715

Line Dancing

Studies in the
Postmodern Theory of Education

Joe L. Kincheloe and Shirley R. Steinberg
General Editors

Vol. 128

PETER LANG
New York • Washington, D.C./Baltimore • Boston • Bern
Frankfurt am Main • Berlin • Brussels • Vienna • Oxford

Wanda Hurren

Line Dancing

An Atlas of Geography Curriculum and Poetic Possibilities

PETER LANG
New York • Washington, D.C./Baltimore • Boston • Bern
Frankfurt am Main • Berlin • Brussels • Vienna • Oxford

Library of Congress Cataloging-in-Publication Data

Hurren, Wanda.
Line dancing: an atlas of geography curriculum
and poetic possibilities / Wanda Hurren.
p. cm. — (Counterpoints; vol. 128)
Includes bibliographical references.
1. Geography—Study and teaching—Canada. 2. Semiotics. I. Title.
II. Series: Counterpoints (New York, N.Y.); vol. 128.
G76.5.C3H87 910'.71'271—dc21 99-34795
ISBN 0-8204-4584-3
ISSN 1058-1634

Die Deutsche Bibliothek-CIP-Einheitsaufnahme

Hurren, Wanda:
Line dancing: an atlas of geography curriculum
and poetic possibilities / Wanda Hurren.
–New York; Washington, D.C./Baltimore; Boston; Bern;
Frankfurt am Main; Berlin; Brussels; Vienna; Oxford: Lang.
(Counterpoints; Vol. 128)
ISBN 0-8204-4584-3

Cover art by Wanda Hurren
Cover design by Nona Reuter

The paper in this book meets the guidelines for permanence and durability
of the Committee on Production Guidelines for Book Longevity
of the Council of Library Resources.

Printed in the United States of America

To Jordan and Mark.
You will always be a part of my dancing.

TABLE OF CONTENTS

FIGURE

ACKNOWLEDGMENTS

All poems and poetic excerpts that appear in this atlas without a source citation are the work of the author. Permission was granted for including poems or passages from the following:

Ted Aoki, *Memorandum*, Vancouver, BC: June 19, 1998. Reprinted with permission.

Poems by Leigh Faulkner from *Where the Fields End: Poems Selected and New*. Copyright © Leigh Faulkner, 1993. Reprinted by permission of Owl's Head Press, Alma, New Brunswick.

Helen Humphreys, *The Perils of Geography*, Toronto, ON: Brick Books, 1995. Reprinted by permission of the publisher.

Wanda Hurren, "def•i•ni•tion*." This material has been reprinted with permission from *Canadian Woman Studies/les cahiers de la femme*. It first appeared in V. 18, no. 2, 3 (1998) "Looking Back, Looking Forward: Mothers, Daughters, and Feminism."

Wanda Hurren, "Living a Landscape of Geometrical Progression." Calgary: *The Prairie Journal of Canadian Literature*, 1998. Reprinted by permission of the publisher.

View from My Mother's House, by Carl Leggo—Killick Press, 1999. Reprinted by permission of the publisher.

Bill New, *Science Lessons*: (Oolichan Books, 1996). Reprinted by permission of the publisher.

The following poems written by the author originally appeared in *Gender, Place and Culture: A Journal of Feminist Geography* (Vol. 5, Number 3) November 1998: "Living in Linear Fashion," "Transit Lines."

Graphic design for the poem "It is Time" (page 56, 57) was provided by Dan Coggins / 2+2=22 Design Inc.

Map Credits:
Permission for the printing of the North Dakota map was granted by the N.D.D.O.T. Any unauthorized reproduction of any parts or the whole are forbidden. Copyright remains with N.D.D.O.T.

Andreas Nothiger, Vancouver Pocket Transit Map. Vancouver: Andreas Nothiger, © Design Pocket Map Art, 1994. Reprinted with permission of the publisher. All rights reserved.

Municipal Map of R.M. of Cambria #6 produced by Dale Shauf. Reprinted with permission.

Thank you, from the bottom of my heart, to my family and my colleagues/friends at the University of British Columbia and the University of Regina for their support throughout the writing of this atlas. Thank you also to the University of Regina, Faculty of Education, for financial and technical support.

PREFACE TO THE ATLAS

. . . like the colouring books of my childhood
long afternoons spent learning to colour within the lines
we spend our lives learning to keep our bodies
living within the lines
on the maps of our territories.

Recently, a Canadian team of young geographers won the "World Geography Olympics." During an interview with the victors on national television, several Olympiad questions were read in order to give the audience an idea of the knowledge required to win a Geography Olympics: "What is the line of latitude located at 23°27' S?; Which is the smallest city in the United States?; Which is the highest mountain in the world?" The three young men had memorized facts and figures, "*and,*" it was speculated, "*they must have read every issue of* National Geographic." While not wanting to diminish the glory of their victory, I was disappointed that the present conception of geography (at least within popular culture) is that of a school subject requiring a great deal of learning the lines—lines of latitude, lines of longitude, time lines, contour lines, boundary lines, river lines, rail lines, trade lines . . .

This atlas was compiled out of a desire to transform the present state of school geography curriculum. Concerning school geography,[1] map skills and a form of disembodied gazing (*Examine the early map and try to predict where the rail line was laid down in the settlement of the West . . .*) receive heavy emphasis. We are led to believe that the world has already been written, and it is our job to read and learn the lines, rather than take an active role in creating and writing lines. It seems that the lines are already drawn. We just need to color in the spaces and understand human settlement patterns and all of the lines that go along with these same patterns. What is not acknowledged in all of this line learning is that as we read and learn the lines, we are, in effect, learning to live and write the world in a certain (disembodied, disconnected, alienating) way; learning to settle into the patterns.

Geography can be thought of as *geo-graphy*, that is "earth-writing." It is my belief that how we *graphy* the *geo* affects and reflects in the same instant how we live in the world. If we graphy the geo in one fairly exclusive, disembodied manner, we risk alienation rather than connection with self and world. I want to write/dance in the spaces between the lines that are written about the world and about curriculum; to consider how this dancing, in effect, writes the world and curriculum. My words and lines placed on the pages of this atlas are an attempt to create spaces for poetic possibilities in how we graphy the geo, and possibilities for geography lessons that attend to embodied[2] knowing within the lines and spaces.[3]

In this atlas, poetic possibilities within the study of geography are considered along two lines of thought. The first has to do with what I am calling a *poetics of the world*, or a *poeming of the world*. The Greek origin of the word *poetics* is the verb *poema, poieein*: to make, compose, create. A poetics of the world in this verb sense is to create or compose the world. I consider possibilities for composing the world through words within the study of geography: *world as/and text*. This consideration of language and the world is consistent with materialist notions of the determining (and not predetermining) role of language in human life.

While geography can be thought of as a poetics of the world, that is, composing or writing the world, my use of the term *poetics* in this composing, creative sense is not to be confused with poetry and poetic language; rather I am acknowledging the performative, political nature of words and texts. That said, however, my second line of thought regarding poetic possibilities does have to do with poetry and poetic prose. I consider possibilities for geography lessons that invite poetic language. So I am exploring poetics as an action: acknowledging the role that words and texts play in our living (and also the role our living plays in giving shape to our words and texts), and then in addition to this, poetics as a form of writing or composing: poetry and poetic language.

José Rabasa contends that there is no recorded history of the atlas as a genre (358). I chose to work with the genre of the atlas for several reasons. In her natural history of the atlas, Barbara Bartz Petchenik tells us that the largest commercial market for atlases is travelers, who use the atlas as a "looking up" tool (54). Roland Barthes's notion of the space of "looking up" in our reading (*The Rustle of Language* 30) is perhaps a convoluted twist on "looking up" places, but this is one of the aims of this atlas. I am providing spaces for readers (including myself) to look up in the reading act. And in that "looking up" space, to acknowledge the rewriting that occurs, and to imagine the rewriting that occurs when any atlas (even one on a classroom shelf) is read.

My choice of an atlas form is also my attempt to do some scribbling—to color outside the lines of what is expected within an atlas; to refute the science and objectivity of the atlas; to explore poetic possibilities. In spite of (because of) the connections between atlases and Western, patriarchal dominance and power (and the connections between academic discourse and Western, patriarchal dominance and power),[4] I am aiming to "write back" by using one of the very forms that has been exclusive and colonizing. I am choosing to compile an atlas that is about the everyday, that presents alternatives to traditional maps and legends, that includes ground truthing as well as bird's-eye views, that explores lines/dancing/spaces. This atlas is intended to be playful (both in the deconstructive sense and in the transgressive sense), poetical, political, and performative.

I am using the notion of line dancing in three ways within this atlas. First of all, because I am inquiring into embodied knowledge within geography curriculum and curriculum theory in general, I want to call the body to mind, and I believe that a reference to dancing does this. Secondly, I consider the line of signification and what happens with word and world and we around this line. I explore the act of signification as a line dance between word, world, and we, and also the notion of word, world, and we dancing around the line of signification. And, thirdly, related to curriculum, I use the metaphor of curriculum as a dance between the lines of planned curriculum and lived curriculum; I note how curriculum can be thought of as line dancing.

This atlas of line dancing, then, is an atlas of a different sort. Theories of language and signification, epistemological considerations regarding both embodied knowing and textual practices, poststructural approaches to writing/reading, an examination of geography curricular materials and the current state of academic geography regarding poetics and embodied knowledge, and my own personal, lived geo-graphies within the lines and spaces all serve to inform this consideration of poetic possibilities within geography teaching and learning.

Speaking of the changing landscape of curriculum theory, Ted Aoki notes how the language of curriculum theory has moved from one of resistance and neo-Marxist critique, a "critical social theoretic language" (*In the Midst* 193) during the 1980s, to one that is grounded in poststructuralist advances, a curricular theorizing that attends to its own languages. He notes a curriculum theory that is "located between structuralist and post-structuralist notions of sign theory" (193), and an attention to the materiality of language. This atlas is located within these same "between" spaces.

The inquiry into poetics and geography within this atlas is informed by poststructural perspectives, and I want to be clear about the "post" part. I do not believe that poststructural is "not-structural." This inquiry into language and geography is an inquiry into structures that have been in place in order to consider poststructures. That is, I am still working with structures when I begin to examine three possible equations for signification/line dancing in the first chapter. Post signifies a linear progression from something to after-something. The something is still there, and it is examined and questioned and given a close reading. New structures emerge from old structures—and that is the "post" part. In my examination of structural semiotics I recognize the structures that are accepted, and then I posit an alternative structure that combines structures but is a new structure. I use the term poststructural to signify a pos(i)ting of alternative structures that serve our purposes in any given field.

Postmodern and *poststructural* and *deconstruction* are terms often used interchangeably; however, this is not the case within this atlas. My reference to poststructuralism is to signal a questioning and close reading of the structures that have been conceived of thus far in our notions of poetics, and also to signal the confusion of domains or the weakening of divisions between signifier/signified and reading/writing (Makaryk 159). So, in the case of semiotics, in order to construct my notion of line dancing (another structure), I start with structuralist semiotics and then imagine "post" structural possibilities.

My use of the term deconstruction in this atlas is to signal a desire for a better world. I do not wish to leave the world in ruins. I do wish to examine closely the worlds we have constructed through texts, and the worlds we have excluded through these same texts. Deconstruction is a way of reading/writing that acknowledges a multiplicity of reading/writing positions on the part of the reader/writer and is a strategy that opens possibilities for more inclusive, equitable world readings/writings. I consider work that has been done on deconstructing maps and atlases as important work to consider within geography curriculum; these deconstructive readings call into question taken-for-granted assumptions about reality.

The argument is often given that poststructuralism or deconstruction or postmodernism in the end leaves the world foundationless, and in a situation where no thing is better than other things. For me, these three terms are affirmative rather than nihilistic. They reveal that all this "naturalness" has been constructed and that we can continue to (re)search/construct the best possible worlds. I do not wish to close down meaning and further inquiry with my research.

Concerning geography teaching and learning, research around poetics is not an area that has been considered in the past. In Joseph Stoltman's summary of research on geography teaching (within the context of social studies education) he notes that most of that research has been carried out through doctoral dissertation research. Concept and knowledge acquisition, map skills development and sequence, and status studies of geography teaching are common research investigations. Recommendations for further research suggest attention to learning outcomes, new technology, new initiatives, and new approaches to teaching within geography teaching and learning (437–447). Effects of duration of treatment in long-term and short-term retention of learning and an inquiry into experiences that will result in spatially accurate mental images of the world are sample recommendations for future research in geography teaching and learning.

While these recommendations sound like they are for a geography from a different world, one of the recommendations from Stoltman's summary does apply to the research within this atlas. Stoltman suggests that "research is needed on geography's role in students' development of a world image that is spatially accurate and intellectually attuned to values, attitudes, and perceptions of one's own country and of other countries and other peoples" (444). This atlas begins one step before his recommendation, in first of all examining geography itself as already a particular world image, already full of attitudes, values, and perceptions; and in addition, a consideration of the effects of geography teaching and learning on perceptions of one's self (in relation to the world and others) is included.

Attending to the language and the words we use to word the world will enhance and transform our geography teaching and learning and our living in the world. Inquiring into poststructural semiotics highlights just how words, worlds, and we are related, and illustrates how we can move away from a perspective that sees geo-graphy as phenomenological enterprise (privileging experience) and from a perspective that sees geo-graphy as palimpsest and intertextual (privileging word/text) into a space between. A space that opens possibilities for poetics and agency in our world writing.

And now, the preface ends where this atlas of line dancing first began to take shape—at an International Children's Festival, on a rainy day in May, in a big canvas tent. We sat on the top bench of the bleachers, waiting for a group of Zimbabwean dancers to appear on the stage. As the dancers lined up on the stage, the lead dancer issued an invitation . . .

> We invite you to share in our dance. When we share our dance with you, you will know something about us, and we will know something about you. Together we can dance around the whole world.

dancers wearing gum boots
stomp out onto the stage
compose a line of colours
and open smiling faces
we clap and cheer and sway
our beating hearts now learning
the rhythm of their souls

Zimbabwean dancers enticed us with the soles of their feet. A dancing crowd began to gather on the stage at the International Children's Festival.

Could I entice you
to enter this dance
a dance of and around and through
words   and   lines   and   spaces?
Could I alter your heartbeat
disrupt your iambic
rhythmic

breathing
with words
placed   here

                and

                                                    here?

Would you share in this dance
through the lines of this text
through the lines of the world
and through spaces
in
between?

A GUIDE TO THE ATLAS

incantation

atlas let the heavens fall around us
and i will hold the world for a while
but not above my shoulders
i would not have the upper body strength
no i will gently cradle the world in my arms
taking my turn i will rotate the earth
give all the territories pleasure
in the soft evening folds of my breasts
while other lands see daylight
even the seas and all the shiny shimmering creatures within
shall have a turn at my bosom
and the axis—i am afraid that will have to go
north south east west shall be no more
i long to warm antarctica
breathe sweet breath on polar ice caps
while greenland iceland
bask in even warmer climes of my bounteous lap below

Elliot Eisner describes research as "reflective efforts to study the world and to create ways to share what we have learned about it." And then he asks us, "What is your conception of research" (*The Promise and Perils* 8)? I like his conception of research, except that I view research as a sharing of what we are learning about the world. I believe research is an ongoing endeavor—always happening. Even in representing or sharing our research the research is happening, and we continue to learn while we share. There is a poetic performance inherent in research.

Della Pollock writes about performative writing and tells us of how words can have double messages on the page. Pollack describes performative writing as evocative and as metonymic writing. It is writing that says and does. It performs at least two things at once "and so refuse[s] identification with a unitary system of meanings" (83). Often a backslash represents this double meaning; the idea of "and/not and" (and here I borrow from Ted Aoki's notions of metonymy). Metonymic writing calls forth the materiality of signs and forms of writing. The forms we choose can perform a multiplicity of writing.

Writing with/about maps is part of the performance in this atlas, and several map-poems are included in order to bring the body into map reading/writing. In the unpublished version of this atlas, these map-poems with transparent overlays of poetic text made it necessary for readers (including myself) to finger and feel the form, and by placing our hands behind the transparent overlays, we brought our bodies to mind in the reading. Within this published atlas, even while the transparent layers are not visible, the map-poems continue to perform several layers of meaning.

Julia Kristeva notes regarding art that "contents are formal and forms are content . . . to work with forms is the most radical way to seize the moment of crisis" (17). While I do not place this atlas within a moment of crisis, within this exploration of geography curriculum and poetic possibilities I have tried to create a way to share what I am learning in a form that is itself a way of learning. The legends (without maps), maps, map-poems, postcards, notes, words, and poems that explore poetic possibilities also perform poetic possibilities. Poetic writing, both in the creative, active sense, and in the genre sense, is a performative writing. Our words perform the research, and (re)present it. Laurel Richardson is a scholar in sociology who uses poetic prose not just to "write up" her research; she considers the writing itself as research. She notes, "Poems can themselves be experienced as simultaneously whole and partial, text and subtext; the 'tail' can *be* the dog" (26).

Throughout this atlas I have included travel notes; documents that indicate to some extent where I have been. James Clifford reminds us of the baggage, the "historical taintedness" attached to the notion of travel: "its associations with gendered, racial bodies, class privilege, specific means of conveyance, beaten paths, agents, frontiers, documents, and the like" (39). While the metaphor of travel does carry with it notions of privilege and gender and imperialistic appropriation and authority, I have included my travel notes as a playful performance in order to question the separation of "being there" and "getting there" that Clifford (23) describes (the metonymical space of being there/getting there; traveling/arriving), as well as to transgress the boundaries of expected discourses, and to acknowledge the language of the everyday in academic places. Many of my travel notes are interruptions. They perform a refusal to construct a smooth, linear journey out of travels that have often been along winding, maze-like trails. They indicate that my research and writing was not a romanticized journey through exotic lands and climes. Notes to pay the Visa™ bill and a fixation with dust and the messiness of my desk (where I sat for many hours throughout my travels) are included to provide some idea of the mundane nature of my travels.

The degree of privilege attached to my traveling depends on with whom and where I am situated. bell hooks reminds us that "theorizing diverse journeying is crucial to our understanding of any politics of location" (*Representing Whiteness* 343). For bell hooks, the metaphor of travel invokes a terror of whiteness, and of traveling through places where she encounters alienation, rather than playful intellectual journeying. After reading the first travel note in this atlas, Ted Aoki noted the fear in my words. Terror is present in my notes. Several travel notes make reference to spatial fears about "where" to place my words. Throughout my academic journey I occasionally feel/fear I am traveling into strange country, or, in fact, remaining on the boundaries of exclusive terra-stories (terror-stories even). Mine has been the terror that the itinerary for my travels will not, somehow, measure up to the patriarchal, epic journeys often expected within the academy.

This atlas of line dancing has three chapters and a supplement. The first chapter is an exploration of semiotic theory and the notion of poetics. I inquire into structures of signification, and the relationship between word and world and we—an important inquiry regarding geography curriculum, and one that has received little attention to date in the North American context. An attention to poetics and language in geography curriculum is an attention to the role of words in our world-making, and the role of our worlds in our word-making. While scholars in Britain and Australia have considered the kind of language used in geography teaching and learning and the effects of this language on our learning,[5] a language and ideology approach, my look at semiotics is a look at structures of language in order to search out spaces for taking an active role in creating words/worlds. Geography itself is considered a poetics of the world.

The second chapter of this atlas is an exploration of school geography as represented in curriculum (as document) and of recent developments within academic human geography writ large. In the search for areas where poetic possibilities can transform curriculum, it is useful to examine what is currently in place within both of these geographical landscapes (curricular and academic). Support for attending to language and writing and embodied knowledge can be found within academic geography, but these concerns have not been included within the curricular planning lines of school geography.

The third chapter of this atlas is an exploration of poetic possibilities on a personal level, where I take advantage of poststructural approaches to reading/writing, and I do some scribbling. Some imagining. It is meant to further illustrate how reading the lines that have been written about the world can become part of an active (re)writing of the world. Cartography is an integral (sometimes the only) part of geography teaching and learning in classrooms. In this third chapter I consider a playful reading/writing of maps, a poetic reading of maps; and here I am using the term poetic in the creative, active, political, personal sense.

In the third chapter I also consider poetry as a language genre in geography teaching and learning, and how poetry makes a space for embodied knowledge. I am not suggesting that we should erase scientific objective language from geography curriculum altogether and replace it with poetic language, but rather that we should examine the language we (teachers, students, texts) use, and make use of as many genres as possible, in order to know and understand and live in the world with a sense of agency and connection.

The supplement to the atlas is a part of the atlas that finishes the form, and was written in an interpretive, poetic, and playful spirit.

While Eisner encourages us to explore the edges regarding research and representational forms, he warns of people (those with whom we share our research) becoming lost, especially those for whom the terrain is new or those who sail by other stars (*The Promise and Perils* 9). This atlas does explore the edges and also the spaces between the edges. On several occasions I did indeed get lost in my travels. I have come to believe that getting lost is not the end of the world. Perhaps it is only the beginning. Maybe this atlas is a book of maps and spaces to get lost in. And, while it is true that stars are for sailing by, they are also for gazing at and wondering.

STARS BURNING

now i am 40
still
i will tell you
on the august edge
of a prairie july
i wonder
if i will ever
see a star burn out
and if i do
what if it happens
to be one from
the big dipper
and in the city
my son wonders
when do they change
the billboard signs
will he ever see them do it
and why is it
only in recent months
when i look at the crescent moon
i see earth shadow
you might not know this:
at this very moment
there are satellites
blinking their way
across night skies

Chapter One
Line Dancing

in the beginning is the wor(l)de:
is there an instant in time/space
when word becomes world becomes
word becomes world becomes . . .
what amazes me
is not the possibility of an answer
to the question
but that wor(l)des exist to ask

In the Beginning . . .

What a coincidence that *word* and *world* are such similar words! One letter makes the difference, and even that letter is coincidental—of all the letters in the alphabet, it most resembles a simple straight line. Rather than accepting a straight line placed between signifier (Sr) and signified (Sd), (Sr|Sd),[6] it seems that we might take a more active role in signification if we consider a poetics of the world; if we attend to Ted Aoki's backslash (Sr/Sd) in the space of the "and/not and,"[7] if we notice how language and meaning dance up and down and back and forth across the line between signifier and signified and between signifier and signifier; how the line itself tips up and down, back and forth in a constant state of performance. It is often said that the map is not the territory, a reminder that we should not confuse the signifier (map) with the signified (territory). Concerning the notion of poetics and the recognition of the role language plays in constructing our realities, I would prefer to say that the map *is* the territory *is* the map *is* the territory. . . . Word and world dance back and forth across the line. A state of flux exists between signifier and signified, and a space of poetic possibility, a state of constant becoming, is present in this line dancing.

In a search for spaces of poetic possibilities in how word and world are related, it is useful to consider theories where language and

signification figure prominently. These theories have not been
included within discussions of teaching geography in classrooms.
Concerning the subject discipline of geography, very little attention is
paid to the act of signifying or to writing in the discipline of
geography. Trevor Barnes and James Duncan note (regarding the
academic discipline of geography) that we have ignored the fact that
"it is humans that decide how to represent things, and not the things
themselves," and that "when we 'tell it like it is' we are also 'telling it
like we are'" (2–3).

Regarding relationships between word and world, I am going to
do some dancing around the lines in the following three equations
that I have adapted from Ted Aoki's "brief excursion into sign
theory" (*Modernity and Postmodernity* 3):

word   = text as representation
.... = the map is *not* the TERRITORY
↑**WORLD**↑   = the word is *not* the WORLD
                       = in the beginning is the WORLD.

← **WORD** →   = text as intertextuality
▬▬▬▬▬▬▬▬   = the MAP *is* the territory
world   = the WORD *is* the world
                       = in the beginning is the WORD.

word / world   = text as performativity
                       = . . . the map is the territory is the map is the . . .
                       = . . . the word is the world is the word is the . . .
                       = in the middle is the wor(l)de

In relation to the above equations, and in order to explore the
possibilities inherent in the relationship between word, world, and we, I
am situating this part of the dance within a mingling of theories of
semiotics, phenomenology, deconstruction, poststructuralism,
psychoanalysis, and personal theories[8] of living and dancing.

In the Beginning Is the WORLD

word
....
↑**WORLD**↑

In this equation (representing a signifying event), the word (Sr) is assumed to be transparent, as is the line between the word (Sr) and the world (Sd). The word allows the world to show through; the word is mimetic of the world. World (Sd) is privileged; its essence shines through the transparent line and is reflected in the word (Sr), or even mirrored in the word. This equation represents Ted Aoki's imaginary formulation of the sign in Discourse A; the discourse of a representational world, where the verticality of metaphor is at play. Within this equation, the dance of signification is one of representation. There are several assumptions regarding the relationship between word and world and where "we" fit in this equation. This equation assumes that language is transparent and objective. "We" is not present in this equation. The world is omnipresent; there is a true essence/world. Words are used to mime or reflect a mirror image of that essence/world.

Conventional scientific discourse is represented by this equation; a discourse that "commonly maintains that subjective experience is 'caused' by an objectifiable set of processes in the mechanically determined field of the sensible" (Abram 66). An exception to this is the thinking of David Abram (who bases his thinking on Merleau-Ponty). Abram believes that we, bodily, are part of the living world, and so part of the primordial essence of world that leads to language. Phenomenology sees language as rooted in our experiences of the world—so first there is the experience, the world, and then language and words grow out of it. However, Abram sees our body as part of the sensuous world; we live in the world and in language. "Ultimately then, it is not the human body alone, but the whole of the sensuous world that provides the deep structure of language" (85).

This equation suggests that words are chosen to mirror the world (text as representation). Barnes and Duncan refer to this manner of (geo)graphic naiveté as the notion that "pieces of the world come with their own labels and writing in geography is just a matter of lining up pieces of language in the right order" (2). Statements within geography curricular documents that discuss the "nature of geography," or the natural environment as different from the social environment (as if geography itself is a transparent category representing a "naturally occurring" subject area/world), would seem to reflect this position. Within geography lessons, words are assumed to represent a privileged world. We are writing about the earth; the earth that already is. There is no acknowledgment that we might be choosing words to represent a certain "construction of the world;" or that our words as we choose them actually play a part in constructing or performing the world; or that, as Derek Gregory notes, the words we use are "not entirely of our own choosing" (quoted in Barnes and Duncan 2).

In the Beginning is the WORD

world

Within this equation, word is privileged over world, and in fact, world becomes erased. This view of signification presents reality as impossible to write—we have images and symbols, but reality is something that will always slip away from us in our attempt to write it. The line between word and world is opaque, and it is assumed that one does not relate to the other—in fact, the word is the world. There is only the word, and the difference between words, to determine our worlds. Ted Aoki calls this the world of "floating discourse," where meaning is constructed in the space of difference between Sr and/not and Sr and/not and Sr.[9] Our worlds are constructed in spaces midst words.

Jacques Derrida is a prominent scholar working under/within this equation. Derrida is famous for his lines about nothing outside of the text, which would seem to be saying that signs would then define us. We cannot come into presence without language. Without discourse. And how did the signs get there in the first place? According to Derrida there is no center, language is a game, a play of signification. He speaks of the absence of any transcendental signified. That is, there is nothing that existed before language and words could signify it. Also, related to this transcendental signified, there is no thing; rather we have a whole world of not things. In the act of signing, meaning is always deferred. What we sign is already different from what we intended to sign and meaning is deferred. There is a lapse. Related to this lapse, Peirce and Benveniste say that the signified itself (in the signifying act) then becomes a signifier and signifies something else (Silverman 14–53).

This equation represents the notion of text as intertextuality, which relates to Barthes's notions in *S/Z* of denotation and connotation (6–9). Barthes noted the existence of an original denotation, which then signifies a secondary signification or what Barthes called connotation. Connotation is the set of cultural codes that takes over from an original denotation.

Perhaps Derrida would say that everything is connotation.

This is also   similar to his idea of traces, and

all   significations   being

Which leads us now,   to metaphoric and metonymic writing.
Discourse C is the Metonymic space of metaphor and metonymy;
        of and/not and . . .   And what about Lacan?
Subjects are mediated through language/signifiers, not signifiers
mediated through subjects.   No, I think today

I cannot write myself out of these circles of semiotic readings.
And readers, you may one day   read
                a continuous, linear text,
        as is expected in some traditional scholarly circles. Must I
language a linear landscape for you? Are you interested in what
happens under the surface?
                        Behind the scenes?
                Between the lines?

What this looked like in its becoming?   An   atlas
                                        performing?

Place: Desk, *Dissemination*

So this is all about language. Playing with language and words in an attempt to question/critique the "status quo" or notions of "truth." But how to play, how to become part of the game? Derrida desires a change of the rules in order to change the game itself. Still another game. And who can play? Must I read Mallarmé, Heidegger, Hegel, and so on in order to have the right to say I won't play? Why am I resisting this text despite my delight in the way Derrida is playing with language and text on the page? Maybe because he is privileged, male, French, "philosopher"? Deconstruction is a privileged game of words? Needing a long and thorough preface by a translator. Derrida refuses to preface. Someone else, a woman, does this in order to disseminate his (Ideas). Again, a sign of privilege.

A word contains phonetic and mental referent? So the word is everything according to this text. I thought a word only *refers* to the mental referent—a word contains only the phonetic signifier that *refers* to a mental signified which depends on the reader of the word—the mental referent is in another body, isn't it? (And "b o d y" calls forth a multitude of possible "mental signifieds," depending on who reads/writes the phonic signifier.)

The whole point of the book seems to be negated by the presence of the translator's introduction. Otherwise, Derrida is only playing with himself (master(de)bating) as indeed he apparently plays with Rousseau's discussion of writing "on the one hand" and masturbation "on the other"! So, the translator, the woman, becomes the "handmaiden" to his "tale"; becomes complicit in his master(de)bations.

Derrida and Geography: His ideas relate to what I might be able to say about form and content, and deconstructing notions about what has been referred to as the "Nature of Geography."

Travel Notes

And is this atlas/research itself a deconstruction of atlas/research writing? Jeff Collins and Bill Mayblin note that deconstruction cannot be described as a project, "if it has an outcome staked out in advance, a goal which predetermines its movements" (95). They also state that Derrida would say "there is no assured essence of anything. If things seem secure and natural, it's because they are governed by a powerful consensus, premised on foundational thinking" (99).

Every misted hollow folds
words over on your tongue.
Like time travel gone wrong,
the perils of geography.
All that old cartography.
O, the New World.

Helen Humphreys

ON FIRST ENCOUNTERING TRACES

at first glance
a form so delightful
words placed   (arbitrarily?)
meaning pure mystery
not unfolding   5
until in sheer distress
the presence of
a comic form
shelved among great works
and Derrida's words   10
manage to
keep open
the idea
that
translations are not copies   15
made to deliver the meaning
of an original
but(t)
other texts
words about words   20
that become words
to write words about
and
Derrida
I shall not   25
fall nor stumble lightly
slide across your words
because
I know their places
in my reading/writing   30
                                             30a spaces/traces of Barthes

I have been blindly
tracing
shadows

Place: Desk, Kitsilano Blenz Coffee Shop, into a bit of Caputo's text

So . . . radical hermeneutics. I am beginning to see how Derrida and Heidegger fit together. Heidegger is saying we still need to wonder about the possibility of Being as presence—he is questioning the presence (the metaphysicalness of Being). And Derrida is critiquing any notion of presence, calling into question, paying attention to ambiguity. Is this ambiguity present? Absent?

So, then, my search for poetic possibilities in geography curriculum is informed by notions held within a radical hermeneutics project. If we open up geo-graphy to uncertainty and ambiguity, do we open up geo-graphy to possibilities—poetic, active, creative possibilities at that?

And what do language and writing have to do with radical hermeneutics (hermeneutics that is open to multiple interpretations)? Writing in geography at that? Well, there is more than one way to write the world. And there is more than one way to read the world as it has been written. We can open up maps and write in some of the absent lines and spaces—lines that are called into presence by their absence.

We can write with a language that calls the body into presence, and illustrate the mind/body-ness of learning and experiencing. We can disrupt polarities and make them *and/not and* spaces. We can learn from ambiguity. By returning to the original difficulties we can say that something is and/not and, we can explore life in the flux.

Today I heard Carl Leggo speak about "Performing in Re-S*earch*: Fifty Ways of Listening to Light." I heard him say "I want" at least 10 times, and then I quit counting. Maybe he even said "I want" more than 50 times. I like hearing what people want. And I like thinking about what I want. So, now, I am going to list some of the things I want.

1. I want to draw attention to how we word-the-world-the-word within geography teaching and learning.
2. I want to bring the body into our teaching and learning and languaging in geography.
3. I want to remind people of their bodies, even as they dance through lines of text in this atlas.
4. I want to speak and write and dance poetically about poetics.
5. I want to sound like I know what I am talking about.
6. I want to look at theories of signification and tie these theories into the study of geography in classrooms.
7. I want to create a bit of unease, some uncomfortable feelings, like the feeling that comes when I say the word body in some places.
8. I want to open up possibilities for earth writing.
9. I want to open up possibilities for research writing.
10. I want to reconceptualize geography curriculum.
11. I want geography lessons to include time for reading/writing poetry.
12. I want geography lessons to include time for re-membering bodies in spaces.
13. I want geography lessons to include time for taking things personally.
14. I want geography lessons to include times for telling and listening to stories about how it feels to be in places.

To be continued . . .

Languaging always emerges and streams from pre/positions located in embodied spaces, in geography . . .

Carl Leggo (*Living Ungrammatically* 175)

Place: Desk, *The Subject of Semiotics*

So, this is all making more and more sense to me gradually. Nice combination of readings: *Dissemination*, *Caged in Our Signs*, and *Subject of Semiotics*. Plus being familiar with Barthes's work helps. Silverman seems to be making the point, or at least it comes up occasionally throughout her text, that there is a relationship between signifier and signified that is back and forth—both are secondary signs in the act of signification.

On Derrida: "Derrida, on the other hand, insists that all signifying terms—signifieds as well as signifiers—are secondary. No absolute distinction can be maintained between the former and the latter, since both carry the 'traces' of all the other signifying elements with which they interconnect" (Silverman 34). (Which relates to my question: Is there an instant in time space when . . . ? Or was there ever a denotating, or is it all connotating?)

Connotation is secondary, it allows for free play, for plurality. "The very authenticity of denotation is called into question—it is charged with being an impostor, a metaphysical fiction which passes itself off as the hearth, center, guardian, refuge, light of truth" (Silverman 32).

Denotation as lines on dictionary pages; we refer to these lines in our connotation? Perhaps both are secondary, or perhaps both are primary. (Except that, as Lacan indicates, words in dictionary definitions are also words that have to be defined on other pages of the dictionary . . . and so on and so on . . .)

I wonder about how we are using the dictionary in all our word play and attention to language, and the throwing away of PRESENCE, and discarding any transcendental signified or essence or "one right answer" or metaphysical presence or you know what I mean; truth, and so on.

Original difficulty, multilayered definitions and word origins, getting to the essence, the original definition. We say we don't like to define, that there are many interpretations, yet we go to accepted, consensus definitions in order to open up spaces of possibility for meaning. Is there some metaphysical presence being called into presence here? In order to return to original difficulty, we use defining mechanisms. To define is to put a boundary on meaning; to limit meaning . . . another and/not and?

Page 9 of *S/Z*: "Denotation is not the first meaning, but pretends to be so; under this illusion, it is ultimately no more than the last of the connotations (the one which seems both to establish and to close the reading), the superior myth by which the text pretends to return to the nature of language . . ."

This sounds like what we think of the dictionary—metaphysical fiction passing as truth. And why are there second and third and fourth, and so on editions of dictionaries? Precisely because we must acknowledge the next connotations. The life of language.

And would radical hermeneutics support the getting rid of notions of denotation and connotation (because connotation also seems to be a closing down of openings, of possibilities for a multiplicity of meanings; the secondary boundary to meaning?) Or is it rather that there are a multiplicity of connotations, and this is all part of the hermeneutic circle?

So we want to stay away from closing readings or closing down possibilities for meaning, or at least be cognizant of the process of trying to achieve this state of making all meanings evident—acknowledge our desire for this? *According to Derrida, all signification is intertextuality in motion? (Did I make this up or read it somewhere?)*

So what does this mean for geography, teaching, and learning?

Language and writing have been recognized by geographers as important to the field of geography. Geography has not previously attended to language/writing. This is the focus of several scholars working in human geography, and feminist geographers attend to the nontransparency of language.

And on into geography curriculum: What does it look like? Does it attend to writing/language? Could it? If we look at curriculum as (. . .) then there are spaces for possibility within geography curriculum. Poetic possibilities: for including a language of theory, a language of poetry, a language of description (related to language of poetry), and a language of everyday places.

at a window counter

> *light is gentle*
> *coming across my page*
> *passing buses*
> *alter sunlight*
> *every ten minutes*
> *breath is visible*
> *surrounding*
> *smoking coffee drinkers*
> *at an outdoor table*

Desk Notes

Place: Desk, *Course in General Linguistics, The Subject of Semiotics*

I want my notes on language and signification to stay in the Travel Notes. So you can see where I have been. After all, I had to start somewhere. You might want to know where I have been.

Saussure (Sr = signifier, Sd = signified, S = sign)

According to Saussure there is no line dancing between Sr and Sd. The relationship between the two is arbitrary.

Is this like a dark curtain between Sr and Sd? No, because he is saying that the phonic component (Sr) calls forth a mental image (Sd). It is just that any given Sign could be made up of any given phonic component that would call the mental component to mind. A tree could be called a gooble.

Here is how I am seeing it:

$$
\begin{array}{cc}
\text{signifier} & \text{signified} \\
\downarrow & \downarrow \\
\text{phonic} & \text{mental image} \\
\downarrow & \downarrow \\
\text{word} & \text{thing or referent: world}
\end{array}
$$

wor(l)d =   word   +   world
            (sign)   (referent)

wor(l)d is a sign for a dancing signification; a sign that acknowledges a relationship between the signifier + signified

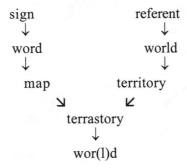

If we acknowledge that *we* tell and listen to these terrastories, these wor(l)ds, then we could add *we* to the equation: w(or(l)d)e = worlde.

Worlde is an acknowledgment of the space between a signification that includes a transparent line between Sr and Sd, and one that includes an opaque line between Sr and Sd; *worlde* stands between, in the space between. Maybe an inter-pretive space, a space standing between.

Geo/graphy sometimes privileges geo (world) and assumes a transparency between Sr (sign) and Sd (referent).

Geo/graphy sometimes privileges graphy (word) and assumes an opaque bar between Sr and Sd, and that Sr and the space of difference between signifiers becomes all important.

We need both: locate oneself in the backslash (Ted Aoki)—between world and language.

How we signify determines our concept of the signified. The signified (mental image Saussure talks about and thing or referent others talk about), or our understanding of the signified, is shaped by the signifier? Not an arbitrary relationship? Not as linear as Saussure envisioned. More circular.

What I don't want to write about is semiotics and the intricacies of index and icon and symbol and the primary and secondary, and metaphor and metonymy in great detail.

What I do want to write about is the line in semiotics, and what happens around it; why it is even there. I will have to discuss the basics of what semiotic equations look like and then consider what happens around the line, and what this means for geography or curriculum or teaching and learning or writing or earth-writing.

Are there spaces, is there a borderland between the two? Close to the borderline is there a borderland? Where signifier and signified are in a state of flux around the line, dancing back and forth, and this is the sign? Actually a dancing back and forth across the line, or a tipping back and forth of the line—the line itself dances, and the signifier and signified dance around it, and in total, it is a dancing sign? The SIGN is a dance, rather than a linear progression of events . . . in the act of signification. Worlde as a dancing sign. Or is it a square dance, with a caller (the SIGN), and we are signs as well? And what do metaphor and metonymy have to do with all this? And desire and lack?

need the light of lamp, yet yellows the desk top   fine cover of dust on everything
*   papers stacked edges flopping curling over cloudy day out the window   CDs*
stacked, sliding   bulletin board full   looking disorganized   Seattle
mug behind printer should get rid of gold dish like the frog though   get   reprints   for
Kathryn and Janet   meeting? supper? pizzas?   file papers
Desk Notes

MY SON TAUGHT ME

about semiotics:
at the age of three he disputed the arbitrary nature of the sign
    I know why ice is called ice—
    *because it **is** just so icy!*
and at his first taste of spinach linguini
declared it *just   too   gishy*

about phenomenology:
in true Heideggerian form
he takes great joy in the thinging of things
    Look at this—you just take this thing, and turn it around this other thing
*and a thing comes out to tie right onto **this** thing!*

about psychoanalysis, desire, and lack:
he volunteers Saturdays at the SPCA
just so he can pull very gently on a leash
he consoles cats
and he dreams of a dog

Structuralist semiotics be damned
he is my son
and he *is* just so sonny

Place: My Desk

Not a good day today. And my desk is a clutter of junk. Much of it someone else's. *Titanic* web site printouts, a Grade 9 science research paper. Already it is necessary, it seems, to define the problem. In Grade 10 they will probably add a new section to the assignment: limitations of the study. Phone numbers and scheduling scribbles for someone else's schedule. Notes and sticky notes here and there.

I am in despair today. Minute differences in the language of signification. Signifier is showing up in disguise as a sign, as an interpretant. And Peirce is saying the signified of the signifier is another signifier with another signified which is another signifier with a new signified and so on. A linear thing, a signified that does not turn back on its own signifier, but refers/relays to another signifier or becomes itself another signifier, delaying meaning further on down the line. A train/chain of signification.

Peirce is not saying what I am trying to say. I am trying to say that there is a back and forth action—if we signify something (with a sign), our understanding of the thing (referent/signified) in some way is influenced by the sign we choose, and before we even choose the sign it has been affected by previous signifieds. Does this happen over time, with us(e)?

In the Middle Is the Wor(l)de

word / world

In attending to the notion of poetics as an active writing, I am not concerned with which came first—the world or the word, and I do not intend to prove the existence of any transcendental signified. And I am not trying to say that we should privilege word over world or vice versa. I am more interested in the mingling and dancing of wor(l)de and what that mingling and line dancing might mean for geography lessons.

This equation for signification is in the space between the first two equations. Not privileging word or world, but recognizing that there is a movement of the line in this equation; it is in a state of flux. There is a dancing back and forth between world and word; the relationship between the two is not static, there is kinesthetic energy in the line. The line is dancing between word and world. A part of the world influences the word and a part of the word influences (our conception of) the world. Regarding "we" or the subject, it seems to me that in the first signifying equation, "we" is outside of the word, in the second equation "we" is with the word, and in the third equation, "we" is in the $w(or(l)d)e$.

What does psychoanalysis have to say about poststructural semiotics and word and world and we? Even within this area there is a direct connection made between who we are and how we are in the world, and the connection is made through words. A basic premise within psychoanalysis is that we are intent throughout life on crossing the line between meaning and being; between the I and the one who says I. While Lacanian theories relate these two separate entities or parts of the self to the separation from the mother and a desire to return to the (w)hole, there is a line acknowledged between the two parts. Often the metaphor of the mirror is used to indicate a separateness in our being; that is, there is a glass surface between the I and the one who says I, between the self and the image of self.

This is similar to a line dance between word and world, as we dance between being and meaning, always trying to merge the two, but acknowledging that the line of signification is there. I think that of particular importance to notions of we and world and word are the notions of similarity and contiguity and metaphor and metonymy found within psychoanalytic theories of signification. In our attempt to cross the line, to merge being with meaning, we make use of similarities and contiguities in our signifying acts. While similarity and metaphor attempt in some ways to mirror ideas and images, to say this is like this (a signifying dance of verticality), contiguity and metonymy recognize the separateness of entities even while they are both part of a whole (a dance between the vertical and horizontal). Metonymy itself is a recognition that there are possibilities for meaning that metaphor or similarities might close down. Metonymy is a way of wording worlds with open possibilities. In a way, when we read metonymic writing or writing that presents contiguous sections of text, it is up to us, the readers/writers, to make the connecting line between the contiguous parts. To imagine the line dancing—dancing a new step.

Regarding poetic language, Julia Kristeva refers to this notion of contiguity. She speaks of certain signifying practices that reach "zero degree of meaning" (22); that is, certain ways of communicating (such as poetry that is elliptical, or "the play of colors in an abstract painting or a piece of music that lacks signification but has a meaning") "that do not refer to a referent or have a precise denotative meaning in the way that signs have referents and signifieds" (21). Kristeva defines these acts of communicating as semiotic, but her definition of semiotic is not the structuralist definition. She defines as semiotic those acts of communication that go beyond language. They are moments of meaning that are not reducible to signs. They exist as moments of meaning only because there is language and a symbolic system.

This third equation of signification is related to the rhizomatic space between the book and the world (Deleuze and Guattari 9). Perhaps, rather than a line that dances up and down, back and forth between word and world, there is a space where a multiplicity of connections is possible "and no radical separation can be established between the regimes of signs and their objects" (11)—between words and worlds. Deleuze and Guattari speak of de-territorialization and re-territorialization as movements connected to each other and rhizomatic—the word could re-territorialize the world, and in so doing, the word becomes de-territorialized, but also, in the same movement, the word is re-territorialized into something else: a becoming-world.

MEANDERING[10]

a metaphor (like this one)
will close a door.

metonymy
is part of more . . .

note punctuation
marks metonymy/metaphor

Place: A Traffic Circle

For the last three months I feel I have been writing in a circle, attempting to get out of it and on with my journey, but I can't write my way out of this circle. Many days I enter the circle from a new point, thinking that day I will finally make it out of the circle, but I am like Chevy Chase in *European Vacation*, caught in a traffic circle, repeatedly saying to his children, "Oh look, kids, there's Big Ben."

I want to move on from semiotics and word/world and look at curricular matters, but I can't seem to say what I want to say (I'm not sure *what* I want to say), and I am now afraid of failing at this whole thing. I keep trying to figure out new ways to organize a discussion of how words and worlds are connected, and each time I get to a point (usually where I have to start talking about theory) where I just don't want to write another word. Maybe today I will find a way out.

I should be explaining why I think we need to look at words and language in the study of geography. I should be talking about the way words and language are not transparent—how the ways we use language and words in geography lessons form a part of our world writing, our geo-graphying.

Why do I keep writing in this travel journal instead of in the "atlas"?

groceries
ink for printer
red tulips
check at library
bookstore
mail VISA™ payment

Place: Desk

Yesterday was the worst day. I just got so frustrated. I think a lot of this frustration has to do with my voice. What do I want this to sound like? I don't want my writing to be obscure or opaque. Last night I was reading a paper by Peggy Phelan on the "unmarked." She was using endnotes, and I think the endnotes were not symmetrical with her actual article. I think she was trying to make a point with them. She was talking about how the generative space is where there is misunderstanding and no way to make things symmetrical. So were her endnotes doing that? Performing asymmetry? And then creating a generative space?

This would be a clever idea, except that I do want people to understand. I liked what Phelan said about the notion of the "Real"—how it is impossible to represent, yet she was desiring that her words on the page would "really" say something. That they would be understood by readers. Even the performance is performed in the hope that there will be some understanding; at least, if nothing else, misunderstanding.

I talked with Anita today about my writing in circles. She said I needed to just leave that section and move on. Go back to it in a week or so and try again. And this is what I will do. I will begin today to explore school geography through curricular documents.

this program teaches and reinforces basic map reading skills   includes material to develop map reading skills   included are a table of contents, map, and

curricular words

Julia Kristeva also notes this generative space and practice in her writing regarding the revolution of poetic language. Along with a space of signification, she speaks of the practice of signification as *signifiance*, an "unlimited and unbounded generating process, . . . a structuring and de-structuring practice, a passage to the outer boundaries of the subject and society" (31). I believe Deleuze and Guattari and Kristeva are also speaking of the mingling dance of word and world in a signifying event.

This notion of rhizomatic growth and its multiplicity of pathways of connections is preferred by Derek Gregory as a way of thinking about geography itself. Rather than conceiving of geography within the "tree of knowledge" framework, as a discipline that is "systematic, hierarchical, grounded—so that its cultivators can scrutinize its fruit, fuss over its pruning, and worry about its felling" (*Geographical Imaginations* x), Gregory proposes that we "open up our geographies to interruptions and displacements, to attend to other ways of traveling, and to follow new lines of flight" (x). Writing in the area of human geography, Gregory would prefer to conceive of geography as a discourse rather than an enclosing discipline. Our habits of mind, and our ways of "making sense of places, spaces, and landscapes in our everyday lives" (11) all combine to provide a discursive framework for geography, one that may open onto spaces for poetic possibilities more so than a framework that is strictly disciplinarian.

Place:(ing) words on pages

This is where I will begin the section on geography curriculum. I have moved this section around quite a bit, splitting sections and leaving spaces. I know my struggle about where to place sections, and even to decide how to split sections, is all about expectations of linearity. It is difficult to make something linear out of something that has not been linear at all in its conception (or in its tracings of tracings). I write in fragments, adding to sections here and there.

A BEDTIME STORY

plot lines:
like isobars
always connecting under the surface
of lives lived in narrative captivity
plot lines:
transform our flat everyday
prairie landscapes
become mountainous terrain
plot lines:
ascend descend ascend
until
at the final cliff we plunge again
into an ending
only to begin
along another linear pathway
plot lines:
perhaps
Aristotle started it all
or maybe
it was manuals
constructing the act of sex
into standard narrative form
or maybe

that is where Aristotle got his plot lines
in the first place
in love with his climax
he chose its topography
and that is why
the ending
always
comes

now
hush my sweet
and go to sleep

And, for example, I do not always remember the places for all of the states in the United States of America, even though I was marked for that in Grade 6. Even though I marked students for that in Grade 6. Even though my own children were marked for that in Grade 6.

Desk Notes

SOUNDING II

when the nurse handed me
my naked little boy child at bath time
i did not know what to do with him
and all of his appendages
all i knew was sisters and girl friends and girl cousins
and mothers and aunties and grandmothers
and great-grandmothers and great-aunties
and how to play dolls and house and hospital
and school
i did not then know the earthy smells of digging deep holes in dirt
and now my son
has a voice that is changing
he bellows and mumbles
and shouts and roars out his new sounds
he likes his voice
he is proud of his rich dark coffee tones
he watches us
he wants to know what his changing voice looks like on our faces
i ask him if it hurts
to have your voice change
what is it like
is it like a sore throat
he laughs at a woman's questions
and says he does not even notice the difference
that i notice
calling home to check on things
he answers the phone
is this my son
i am shocked
and then i think
how silly
of course i know what it is like
to have a voice change
mine is changing also
daily
in this place   and i like it too.

CHAPTER TWO
LANDSCAPES OF GEOGRAPHY

do not be fooled
into believing
borderlines
are imaginary
lines
on maps
and nothing else
they are real
I know a place
a borderline
between
where two countries end
there
is a space
a borderland
wheel tracks in a ditch
we used to go there
on warm summer evenings
park the car
open the windows
welcome the breeze
there
we crossed real
imaginary lines
on over under
into
between
where two countries end
there
is a space
a borderland

Dancing Curricular Lines/Spaces

Ted Aoki invites us to open up to possibilities concerning the meaning of curriculum. He speaks of a curricular landscape consisting of "both planned curriculum and live(d) curricula, as many as there are teachers and students, indeed, a multiplicity of curricula" (*Modernity and Postmodernity* 1) and invites us to enter the space between. To enter the space of the "and/not and." Again I am reminded of the backslash he draws between signifier and signified, signifier and signifier—the sign of the and/not and. Ted calls this a generative space. The space between the lines planned and live(d).

This atlas is an exploration of curricular possibilities within this generative space. But (I have pondered) how do I get to that space? I think I am, and all of us are, always in that space, as we dance up and down, back and forth, between the planned lines and the lived lines. It is in that dancing that curriculum is/happens. Curriculum as living and planning is a dance of performing. Within this consideration of poetic possibilities, I am considering the lines of curriculum-as-planned and the lines of curriculum-as-lived, from the space between the two. Perhaps by exploring the boundary lines, the spaces for poetic possibilities will become evident. By choosing the space between, we are able to imagine possibilities for planning and living, all the while acknowledging and accepting the messiness and ambivalence and chaos of that space. Curriculum is like a dance of planning and living and ambivalence in between. In our dancing, we are adding to the multiplicity of ways the world of curriculum theory can be written.

Curriculum is about self and world. Bill Pinar and colleagues describe curriculum as the medium in and through which "generations struggle to define themselves and the world" (848).[11] Both curriculum and geography hold possibilities for enhancing our notions of self and world. The self and world of curricular lines are shaped by lived experiences (of living, breathing bodies). Curricular lines are lines of self and world, mingling together. It makes no sense to first talk about planned lines, and then talk about live(d) lines of curriculum, because these lines of curriculum are always already mingling and dancing. My exploration acknowledges the dancing that always already happens. And this is not much different than what I have said earlier about word and world. Curricular planned lines are documents of words all gathered together, and these words do influence the live(d) curricular world of geography education. Just as our living influences how we live in the curricular world.

My use of the term *landscape* in regard to geography and curriculum is a conscious effort to call forth the constructedness of both entities. Geography and curriculum are not naturally occurring phenomena. Both are culturally constructed. My reference to planned curricular landscapes is a reference to landscape as an act of observing and as an artifact that is observable. That is, the landscape of curriculum-as-planned is a conscious arranging for a certain effect, and the landscape of curriculum-as-planned is an artifact that is observable. In performative terms, the curriculum-as-planned landscape is an act and a seeing/scene.

Gillian Rose discusses the use of the term landscape within cultural geography. She notes that landscape "refers not only to the relationships between different objects caught in the fieldworker's gaze but that it also implies a specific way of looking" (*Feminism and Geography* 87) and that "whether written or painted, grown or built, a landscape's meanings draw on the cultural codes of the society for which it was made" (89); it "represents only a partial world view" (91). Rose expands on the gendered nature of landscapes (the act of viewing and the scene/seen), noting that the act of viewing was/is masculine (and active), and the scene/seen is feminine (and passive).

Denis Cosgrove's deconstruction of the landscape idea indicates that while the present uptake of landscape within cultural geography is antiscientific, historically landscape represented an objective measuring and linear perspective, and "like the practical sciences of the Italian Renaissance, was founded upon scientific theory and knowledge" (46). It was not considered a partial view at all, but an all-encompassing view. He cautions cultural geographers to pay attention to the particular view they are calling up when they employ the term landscape. He notes an "inherent conservatism in the landscape idea, in its celebration of property and of an unchanging status quo, in its suppression of tension between groups *in* the landscape" (58).

In my initial use of the term landscape in regard to curriculum, I had not considered these aspects, but in retrospect, these geographical musings regarding the term landscape are also quite fitting for curricular musings and the metaphor of landscape. Curriculum (in design and content) is very much a culturally arranged document that reinforces and maintains dominant patriarchal cultural ideologies and a status quo, and in document form (while not necessarily feminine), attempts the linear perspective of which Cosgrove speaks regarding the historical aspects of landscape. However, my present exploration of curriculum, my own arranged view on the pages of this atlas, is a partial view, and thus fits with the current uptake of this term within cultural geography. And if anything, I am trying to disrupt the status quo with my landscaping.

Related to the notion of landscape as view, accounts of spatial representation within the project of modernity include the need to gain a bird's-eye view of specific sites and places, the need to know the world through the gaze—the gaze becoming the claim to knowledge. Gazing from on high allows the viewer a position of power, and the assumption is that by seeing the city or a place as a whole, as a totality, we can then claim to know the city or the place. In the nineteenth century in Paris, hills were built up so that an all-encompassing, distancing gaze was possible. In the 1870s towers began to appear in Western "world" cities (Paris, New York, London), thus facilitating the attempt to organize the world—make it visible and ordered. The view from on high became the all-knowing gaze. Along with the gaze from on high, Benjamin[12] noted that the gaze in nineteenth-century Paris had become mobilized. It became possible to effect the gaze not just from on high, but by moving through the city and observing people in public places: the gallery, the shopping mall, the boulevard. This mobile gaze was made possible through the act of *flânerie*.

Paris, in the nineteenth century, was the birthplace of *flânerie*: the practice of distanced, detached sightseeing. The *flâneur* was gendered (male) and privileged, passing the time among crowds and in public spaces observing life in a detached fashion. More than just an aimless stroll in the park or along the boulevard, Shields notes, *flânerie* was enacted in specific public spaces and involved the art of the gaze:

> The *flâneur* is out to see and be seen, and thus requires a crowd to be able to watch others and take in the bustle of the city in the security of his anonymous status as part of the metropolitan throng. The crowd is also an audience. *Flânerie* is thus a crowd practice, a connoisseur's 'art of doing' crowd behavior. (65)

For the most part, the view from on high, or the detached gaze of nineteenth-century *flânerie,* has been the approach to curriculum in the twentieth century; coming to know something through an objective, disembodied, scientific approach. The curricular tradition within geography itself has been to stand back and objectify places, to study places in a removed sort of way. Curricular *flânerie* is evident in the following lines of Carl Leggo's poem "Grade Four Geography":

In grade four geography
I saw illustrations
Of 10-year-old children;
for all their differences
they looked the same
like Barbie dolls
with interchangeable costumes

. . . .
In grade four geography
I knew the earth was an object
solid, stable, static,
easily described
the earth present
in the words
and pictures and maps
of my textbook (lines 11–17, 25–33)

Returning to Gillian Rose's discussion of landscape and masculinity, Rose notes that feminists have tried to call attention to the masculine gaze that in effect "constructs access to knowledge of geography," a gaze that determines "what are constituted as objects of knowledge, whether environmental, social, political or cultural" (*Feminism and Geography* 109). I would add that this masculine gaze also *constricts* what counts as *ways of knowing.* Rose notes how feminists attempt to disrupt the hegemonic way of seeing within geography, "without imposing an alternative which could only assert a specific femininity as universal in an equally repressive manner" (112). On the following pages, then, I plan to arrange some geographical landscapes, both curricular and academic; sometimes as a traveler/dweller, sometimes, perhaps, as a tourist, and always with possibilities in mind. While my views might appear rather *flânuer*-like on occasion, I do hope to arrange some of my landscapes from the ground level, with more of the detail and more of what Rose refers to as the "small-scale pleasures" (112) being my focus.

Two Landscapes

Geography as a curricular subject has been studied in classrooms across North America since the beginnings of public education. Occasionally a subject in its own right within some school districts, geography is most often included under the interdisciplinary umbrella of social studies education or civics education in elementary and secondary classrooms. Decisions regarding what to teach in geography lessons are based, in part, on state-determined curriculum requirements. And these state-determined curriculum requirements are based, in part, on the academic discipline of geography as it is constructed within scholarly research and writing (most typically originating within geography departments on university campuses) and on the subject discipline of geography as it is constructed within scholarly research and writing (most typically originating within curriculum and instruction departments on university campuses). And here, I think, is another generative space or borderland, and one in which I am presently situated—the space between the lines of curricular geography/social studies education, and the lines of academic geography.

In his studies of the evolution of disciplines and school subjects, Ivor Goodson examines the relationship between academic disciplines and school subjects. While a common understanding of how a school subject evolves is one based on the idea that "an intellectual discipline is created by a community of scholars, normally working in a university, and is then 'translated' for use into a school subject" (4), Goodson notes that this is not the case for school geography. During the late nineteenth century, geography in Britain was struggling at the universities but was receiving more and more emphasis in the schools.[13] Part of the struggle for the discipline within the university context was where to locate geography—it seemed to contain properties that would place it within the humanities and also properties that would place it within the natural sciences. Where it was located (in which faculty) determined the focus of study and the examinations;

thus there seemed to be no consistent approach or growth to geography as an academic university discipline.

School geography during this same time period was an established subject; however, it was growing and changing into a subject area that was so broad and all-encompassing that it was losing its definition of purpose. Goodson's study cites Honeybone as stating that by the 1930s, geography "came more and more to be a 'world citizenship' subject, with the citizens detached from their physical environment" (64). School geographers began calling for a strong academic geography at the university level with the hopes that this would raise the standards and confine the focus of school geography, as well as provide a training ground for future geography teachers.

As a result of pressure from the schools, university geography did become well-established as a legitimate discipline by the early 1940s, and soon specialists were heading school departments. It appears that this is when the gap between the two landscapes began to widen. When it did become established as an academic discipline in university territory, and did indeed train teachers, geography was criticized by other university disciplines for being a subject for children in schools! Perhaps because of this, the academic discipline became increasingly intellectual and rigorous, splitting into specialist areas, each with its own jargon. (And here I am speculating, but at this point, the academic discipline did not likely have the training of teachers high on its list of priorities.)

So, while never quite the same thing, school geography and academic geography have had a longstanding relationship of sorts. What Goodson refers to as a "pattern of disciplines translating down" (from academic scholars) to lower-status groups at the school level (teachers and students!) did not seem to be the case for geography. He refers to the way geography as a curricular area became established as a process of "aspiration upwards" (78).

I prefer to think of the establishment of this curricular area as a mingling process. Most certainly, academic scholars and curricular scholars and classroom teachers and students are each individual determining factors regarding school geography. However, aside from technological advances in approaches to information gathering and processing, over the last 30 years it seems that as curricular scholars,[14] we have not attended to recent developments within the academic discipline. It is a case of being stuck in the 1960s. And here, I think, is

a good place to begin to describe my travels through these two
landscapes. I will start with my travels through the curricular
landscape of geography, and then I plan to share with you some of
the recent developments within the academic geography landscape.

A Landscape of Curricular Geography

What is geography, then, within the lines/spaces of curriculum? As a
subject under the curriculum umbrella of social studies education,
how is geography constructed? How is social studies education
constructed? What are the textual practices supported and promoted
within this subject discipline (as perhaps a way of disciplining
subjects)? In my exploration of the above questions, I am considering
the following planned lines and spaces of curriculum: teacher
education textbooks, social studies documents (ministry and state
curriculum guides) and curricular discussions within recent publications regarding current trends and issues in social studies and
geography education. In exploring these planned lines of curriculum,
my intent is not to offer a detailed analysis of these curricular
materials, but rather, to use these documents to arrive at a description
of how geography is constructed within the subject area of social
studies, to note any attention to textual practices these documents
support, and to explore how word and world and we occur within
geography curriculum. I believe that some form of description of
curricula currently in place is necessary in order to imagine possibilities for change. Parts of these documents appear throughout the
lines and spaces of this atlas, perhaps

*Have students construct glossaries that define environmental terms
associated with resource management (e.g., sustainability,
stewardship).*[15]

*Have students represent what they see when looking down on several
objects (bird's-eye view) on their desk.*[16]

juxtaposed with alternative documents, or I may insert planned lines to
interrupt and/or introduce spaces of possibility.

*Geography and environmental education are obviously linked.
These pupils have become aware of this by studying animal habitats.*

What is not obvious is that the study of the environment begins with your own body: what you do to it, what you do with it, and what it does to the environment. [17]

The geography of social studies education. In this atlas, geography is considered along several lines of thought regarding social studies education (the place where geography is located curricularly). First of all, the geography of social studies education, that is, how it is constructed as a subject area, is considered. What does the landscape look like? And, within this landscape of social studies education, how are geographical understandings and concepts included? What sorts of textual practices are supported through the teaching of these concepts? What are these concepts?

Also, regarding the geography of social studies (and I have been playing with this metaphor throughout my travels), I am considering geography as geo-graphy: earth writing or world writing. Metaphorically speaking, I am concerned with how we *graphy* the *geo*, how we *write* the *world*, within geography lessons and social studies education. Do we privilege word or world, or do we acknowledge the line dancing of wor(l)de? By what we study and how we study in social studies and geography teaching and learning, we are actually poeming the world; we are writing the world in certain ways, and further, we are writing ourselves into the world in certain ways. Teaching any subject is a sociotextual event, and as teachers and students, we write/read ourselves into/out of that text. Curricular considerations need to acknowledge this line dancing.

So, then, how do we word the world of social studies education?[18] What does the landscape look like? There has been an ongoing debate among educators as to what social studies is and what it should be. Several definitions of social studies education focus on the physical and social environments and how people interact within those environments. I do not intend to argue for what I believe social studies education should be. I am basically happy with what it is. I like all the words we use to word the world of social studies education. Regarding geographical understandings within social studies, I am interested in changing *how we say the words*, rather than in changing the words themselves. Despite the arguments about what social studies education is or ought to be, geography is always included in some way as part of social studies education. This atlas provides a general overview of social studies education, and then takes a closer look at how geography occurs within social studies education.

I have included a landscape of elementary social studies education on page 45 (see Figure 1). This is the landscape that I have been traveling through for many years; as an elementary and secondary student, as a teacher education student, as a classroom teacher, as a graduate student, and as a social studies curriculum instructor in teacher education programs. I chose the words for this landscape from state curricular documents, from teacher education resources, and from scholarly writing in the area of social studies education. Most of these words come from definitions and rationale statements for social studies education, and some come from lists of concepts believed to be integral to teaching and learning in social studies. I believe these words are full of poetic possibilities.

I have added the word *inclusiveness* to this landscape. Although it is not mentioned specifically within rationale statements and definitions, the intent in including multiple perspectives, decision making, valuing self and others, and so on, is inclusiveness. What I mean by inclusiveness here, is the idea that social studies is about including all people and places in our conception of the world and how we live in it. Inclusiveness in social studies is about including perspectives from various locations regarding issues that we study in social studies; for example, it is about including an acknowledgment of our emotions and feelings when we make our "reasoned" decisions, rather than ignoring this added dimension. Inclusiveness in social studies is about gender inclusiveness; for example, including both boys and girls in a discussion of what "all thy sons command" means in a national anthem. Inclusiveness in social studies education is about including as many approaches to learning as possible; for example, validating what we know from our bodies and in our hearts about what it is like to live in a community. Inclusiveness in social studies is about including discussions about race and color in our attempts to understand who we are and how we are in the world as individuals and as groups. Inclusiveness in social studies is about including, within our multiple perspectives, a critical examination of those perspectives regarding the welfare of all people; for example, including a discussion of why books about homosexual families are banned from school districts and how we decide on our personal stance regarding these issues.

A LANDSCAPE OF SOCIAL STUDIES EDUCATION

Inclusiveness

Multiple Perspectives   **Location**

Relationships:
physical environment   **Identity**
social environment

Citizenship   **Critical Thinking**

Value and Respect for Self/Others

Making Connections   **Making Decisions**

Respect for Human Equality and Cultural Diversity

Figure 1: A Landscape of Social Studies Education

Let me relate what I have noted in my travels through the landscape of social studies education. Within teacher education materials and government curricular documents, social studies is actually organized geographically. That is, we begin with studies of our immediate surroundings in the primary grades and we move further and further out into the world as we grow up. This method of organization is referred to as an "expanding horizons" approach. The expansion outward generally organizes study at the kindergarten and Grade One level on self and family, the Grade Two and Three focus is on communities, first the local community, and then neighboring communities. Grade Four is usually a regional study, Grade Five is a study of the nation, Grade Six focuses on neighboring countries, Grade Seven often has a global focus, and Grade Eight through Twelve varies, but often includes a study of society and civilizations. So, then, from primary to intermediate and on into secondary education, social studies education becomes more and more removed from the local and personal.

While documents note the importance of making connections between the global and the local, social studies education is described within documents as a study that moves from the local to the global. A recent assessment of social studies includes the following recommendation regarding instruction at the Grades Five–Seven and Eight–Twelve levels: "Increased emphasis on relating material studied to the individual student's life."[19] This does not show up as a concern for Grades K–Four, where study is more focused on the local and the personal.

This geographical organization of study supports a notion that as we grow older it is desirable to move away from the personal, private spaces to the public spaces. So, geographically, social studies promotes, in the way it is organized for instruction, a split between public and private. There is also a gender difference regarding this demarcation of the study of private and public. Students in primary classrooms are more likely taught by women, and they study the more private spaces—home and family. Students in intermediate classrooms and secondary classrooms study the less personal, more public spaces and places, and are more likely to be taught social studies by both men and women.

As social studies education progresses through the grades (or as children progress through social studies education), children are encouraged to adopt a bird's-eye view in their study of the world, especially, as will be noted further, in the case of "map skills." This method of detached study reminds me of a poster advertising the discipline of geography. The poster depicts a young man with his arms and legs wrapped around a flag standard that is at the top of a skyscraper and he is looking down on the world of the city below. The caption on the poster says: "See the world from a different place. Become a geographer." I am hopeful that we can also be geo-graphers at the ground level.

Place: Desk

Like Hélène Cixous, I make many of my notes at night. Many nights while "I am in my bed in a greater proximity to my body" (106), I get up and go to my desk to write a note. And in the morning I work my notes into my text. I expand on them. Now I am expanding.

In the night I made notes about topography. I am not happy with the way I have been writing the curricular topography over the last few days. I don't like trying to string along artificially a group of thoughts that did not occur in a nice long linear string. What if I started writing like Baudrillard? What if I wrote cool memory fragments about curriculum and geography and wor(l)de? And left spaces between the fragments? Would that be democratic? Would readers feel misled? Or would they feel free to make their own rhizomatic connections?

Fragmented writing is what these travel notes sometimes portray, or at least they will perform this when they are placed within the "real" book pages. But *where* to place them is the question.

She has been warned of the risk she incurs by letting words run off the rails, time and again tempted by the desire to gear herself to accepted norms. But where has obedience led her?

Trinh T. Minh-ha (264)

Description: [20] *A Legend of Exploration into Geographical Spaces* [21]

In the years of my research and teaching, I set out to explore the occurrence of geography teaching and learning within the lands of social studies education. Here is a listing of my various ports of call:

Cool Memories and Dreams of Teaching and Learning Geography
Teacher Education Texts
Recent Publications in Social Studies Education
Government Documents [22]

Having my supplies made ready, I departed one evening with only a soft breeze to fill the sails of my sloop. Having set my sails for a close haul sail, I cleated the jib and mainsail sheets, which then left my hands free to work the tiller. Soon a landscape was visible in the distance, a fragmented archipelago.

My first sighting of geography teaching and learning was along the islands of teacher education textbooks. Having already been to parts of these islands in the past, I was familiar with some of the chapters included within each of these islands, and each one included geography as one of the disciplines of the multidisciplinary subject of social studies. Within these chapters, the value of geography was expounded, evidence of which follows:

> "The teaching of geography and map skills plays a crucial role in Social Studies" (Wright 141).

> "Effective, efficient communicators and decision makers must know about the world around them. Understanding geography helps develop perspectives on our changing world and provides a better understanding of world cultures" (Maxim 357).

> "Geography is a critical concern, everything that happens on this planet has a geographic component. . . . Humanity faces a crisis in the management of the planet Earth" (Kirman 100).

A chapter with the name of Field Research had a strong local environmental education focus. There were eighteen suggested activities for a local field research study, and two of these spoke of embodied knowledge:

> 14. List all of the sounds you can hear and smells you can smell. Where do they come from?

15. Write descriptive words or sentences about how you feel at the site. Does it make you feel happy, sad, angry (Wright 137)?

Wright describes "getting a feel" (135) for a place as a major goal of field studies, along with collecting data firsthand and teaching map skills. There was a very wide and strong stream running through this chapter on field studies, and it can be described as "how people use and manage the environment." I noted the following textual practices encouraged within the field study samples: draw, list, write descriptive words or sentences.

In many places along the islands of teacher education textbooks, the teaching of map skills could be seen, and the teaching of latitude and longitude was the most prominent feature among these skills. Indeed, teachers were encouraged to begin the study of a place with the latitudinal position of that place. A "pilot's-eye view" (Wright 147) is one perspective children are to develop regarding geography and map skills, and this same pilot's-eye view is evident in the way illustrations are presented in these chapters. My eyes never wearied of photographs that looked down on drawings or maps. On the 163rd page of this chapter, I noted a suggestion that children should read "accounts of the physical and cultural landscapes of a place in order to get a 'feel' for the location."

Kirman describes geography as a "subject that is very skills-oriented, but those skills will help in some areas of decision-making, provide a geographical foundation for examining local, national, and global events, and serve a pupil for a lifetime" (107). His chapter on mapping provides space-age images and promotes an "astronaut's-eye view" (111).

Several chapters along these islands link geographical skills with environmental education, and there is a focus on problem solving and managing the planet earth. A concluding comment within one chapter on environmental education calls for

> an appreciation of nature, and the recreational and esthetic enjoyment of our environment. Art, poetry, music, meditation, and physical activities are expressions of this appreciation. . . . The idea that we should take time to smell the flowers and listen to the birds could well be an environmental objective. (Kirman 106)

* *

Cool Memories and Dreams I
Teacher Education Classroom

I invited Warren to come and talk with my teacher education students about bodies, spaces, and drama in our social studies curriculum class. He came to class today and shared some of his ideas with us. We used our bodies within our classroom space to map/locate our home places, and also in some way to represent our place. Two students and myself were from the prairies—we grouped together according to our geographical region. We decided to use the entire room to depict our place. The three of us spread out in the room and held out our arms. We were lonely trees on the prairie.

One of the "prairie trees," a tall quiet man, said to me, "I hate doing things like this." He was very shy and held up his arms self-consciously. He was a perfect tree for our self-conscious prairie landscape. A few weeks later, when he handed in his portfolio, he had reflected on the experience of using his body to represent a place. In his portfolio, he outlined an idea he had for using Warren's approach to bodies and mapping in a physical education lesson on lines of movement in space.

Children sit in the middle of this maelstrom, full of belly giggles and little night tremor jolts, waiting for us to respond in kind.
Waiting.

David Jardine (135)

* *

Along one of these islands, I encountered a cautionary note from June Chapin and Rosemary Messick, regarding overemphasizing map skills. These authors tell us that "too often only map skills are stressed rather than all the major concepts of geography" (176), and that school textbook authors are attempting to incorporate more contextualized studies wherein map skills are applied to real-life problems and issues.

Making a stop along an island devoted to the current state of social studies education, I located one chapter that dealt specifically with geography. Elspeth Deir describes geography as "an integrated discipline that provides knowledge of our planet's physical and human systems, knowledge that can equip us to make wise decisions about our use of the Earth" (131). A common stream that ran throughout this chapter and gathered force along the way was the stream of problem solving along with geographic tools, knowledge, and skills.

On this particular island, computer applications, World Wide Web access, satellite imagery, and digital technology were held in high esteem, and Deir notes that because of these technological advances geography could be on the same level as math and science. Because of these advances, Deir believes that students and parents will perceive geography as a "'hard science,' and therefore of value" (132).

After traveling along these islands of teacher education textbooks, I continued on in my exploration, with social studies curriculum guides[23] appearing on the far horizon. Geography was evident within these documents/islands in the form of general themes and specific concepts and understandings and skills. Features of a landscape, regions, map skills, location (finding), distribution of resources and people, size and structure were all seen along these curricular document islands. Geographical features and regions were understandings that were emphasized.

Regarding textual practices that are supported within the study of geography in these social studies curriculum documents, the following is a listing of those noted: observe and record on charts   label continents and oceans   read stories to students   present research through models or maps that use a variety of grids and scales to show location   debate   log daily resources used by your family   write or give oral presentations on reducing levels of resource consumption   locate and display features on a map   write letters   create models

* *

Cool Memories and Dreams II

Teaching and Learning and Living on the Edge of Pink

In September
I tried not to press too hard
on the tips
of my freshly sharpened Laurentien pencil crayons
colouring the world
I saved my favourite colours for the big spaces
USA was #5 Purple
#4 Cerise was for the British Commonwealth of Nations

If I was just colouring Canada
#1 Deep Yellow was for my province
    a place where men in malls in winter
    had #17 Smoke Grey coats, hair, whiskers, and skin
Manitoba was #10 Brown
Alberta was #2 Orange
    the colour of the Camrose grain elevator on our calendar
    beside the fridge
Quebec was #16 French Green
British Columbia was #22 Sky Magenta
I would have chosen #9 Deep Green because of all the trees
except that I always saved #7 Peacock Blue for the ocean
I thought there was a rule about green and blue
not going together: *Green does not go with blue*
my older sister told me one school morning
eyeing my carefully chosen pedal pushers and pop top

In July
living on #22 Sky Magenta
sailing in #7 Peacock Blue
my husband takes the tiller and moves us through the waves
as if we are on the #1 Deep Yellow space of a prairie wheat field
instead of leaving a #10 Brown line
of astonishingly moist overturned soil
behind us in #7 Peacock Blue
we leave a #23 Cotton White line of air mixed with water

* *

of structures draw pictures of people who work in different environments include thinking bubbles flag, label and locate historical and current events on a map develop a collage read poems about the environment write poems about the environment role-play.

During my travels through these curricular documents I encountered occasional definitions of geography, and here are samplings of their words:

> *[Geography is] "an integrative discipline that brings together the physical and human dimensions of the world in the study of people, places, and environments. Its subject matter is the earth's surface and the processes that shape it, the relationships between people and the environments, and the connections between people and places." (Geography Education Standards Project 18)*

> *"Geography is a discipline that integrates many subjects and addresses both the physical and human-created systems of the world in the study of people, places, and environments. With the widespread depletion of the earth's resources due to rapid population growth and resource mismanagement, there is a need for a society that is geographically literate and therefore able to make informed decisions about the sustainability of the earth's resources and the future of the planet." (British Columbia, Grade 12 Instructional Resource Package, 1)*

* *

Cool Memories and Dreams III
Teacher Education Classroom

They do not understand the point of teaching time zones. Every year it is the same thing. I warn students ahead of time about the chapter in the textbook. They become very confused with the explanation of how to teach time zones. I tell them that every time I taught time zones in social studies classrooms, I had to figure it all out and describe it in a way that made sense to me before I could teach it. And I lived in a place where time did not change, if you stayed in the same place. But if you crossed a line, then you had to understand the way time changes. Time zones is a very abstract notion. The world was divided into 24 time zones in 1884. Imagine the moment when time in the zones began!

Erika introduced me to Marilyn Singer's book, *Nine O'Clock Lullaby*. It is a wonderful poetic journey around the world. Great for teaching time zones, and students could write some of their own poetic lines about the zones.

. . . teaching them as we do to climb up into their heads and join our frightened numbers, our sad enumerations. Earth becomes mathematized and things don't quite add up any more.

David Jardine (140)

* *

It is Time.

excuse me but
now
i have to tell you
time
does not happen in zones
and the line across
the pacific ocean
is not really the place
where
monday begins
when sunday ends

what time is it mister wolf
they stand on a green line
dancing with anticipation
shrieking with delight
at the stroke of midnight
he comes chasing
and they race back to homefree
wanting so much to be caught
and eaten alive

As lands to the east

are ahead in time

and lands to the

west are behind, it

is afternoon to the

east and morning

to the west

what time is it mister wolf
a body mind exploding erasing
breathing in between
caught again
in expectation
breathe now breathe
another life from my own
from our own
your quick breath now
and the squeal of shock
when it is over when it begins

what

time is it

the silence of words that tumble
and pile all together

mister

in a heap
when a mother tells a daughter

wolf

a father has slipped away

after all that

anyway

Students
should know
time does not happen in zones

you only lose

now

one whole day

you'd better run

if you cross the

before i eat you for my supper

line at midnight

A common sight on my travels through these various geographical spaces within social studies education were the words "Map Skills." The textual practices encouraged were largely labeling and listing and some describing activities. Along these islands I was treated to bird's-eye views and pilot's-eye views and astronaut's-eye views, and many times had the sensation of flying in a detached way up above the world. Looking down on lines and spaces.

A problem-solving approach to geography teaching and learning was emphasized. Geography was constructed as a tool or body of knowledge for making decisions and solving problems, mostly management problems.

I noted evidence of statistical texts, impersonal geographies, moving from concrete to abstract in our study of our world and from local to global. Environment was spoken of in terms of management, and geographical "systems" were split into human and physical. Concerning geography, "getting physical" seemed to imply detaching ourselves from any physical contact with the world, and "digital" analysis had nothing to do with our digits actually mucking around in our surroundings; rather our digits poke at keys on a keyboard and mess around with numerical digits.

A Landscape of Academic Geography

For the most part, my travels through this landscape were chosen to support my inquiry into poetics and out of a desire to transform geography curriculum. While I will highlight current major attractions within the academic geography landscape (because I believe within the curricular context these attractions have gone unnoticed, and they are attractions that would enhance the curricular landscape in many respects), I do intend to focus on the regions related to poetics (language and reading/writing and texts) and to some extent, embodied knowledge.

A guide who has been most helpful to me throughout my travels in the academic landscape of geography is Derek Gregory, along with his book *Geographical Imaginations*. Published in 1994, this book offers a comprehensive overview of contemporary issues in spatial studies, with the first section reporting on how geography has recently evolved. Three tenets that guide Gregory's own geographical imagination and his passages through a critical human geography relate directly to my own inquiry into geography curriculum and poetics and embodied knowledge. Gregory posits that geography (as an area of study) must examine closely and not take for granted "the

Travel Notes

Place: Harbour Centre, Simon Fraser University

Went with Pat to hear Derek speak at Harbour Centre. On the way we stopped in at Spartacus and Pat showed me a book, *Maps Are Territories: Science Is an Atlas*. Very interesting little anecdotes about mapping traditions and beliefs.

Derek's talk was very engaging. And interesting use of visuals along with his talk. Somewhat montage in the way they spliced his words, although illustrations were congruent with his words, not actually disrupting them. The de Certeau citation was perfect for his talk, except that I still think it calls forth the notion of landscape as text. Derek pointed out the difference between textual representations of landscape and landscape as text, indicating he sided with the former. But, I see a mingling, between textual representations and the referent, between word and world. It is possible to consider landscape as text, not just as represented in text. That is, in our textual representations of landscape, landscape becomes a text? Or at least has some pretty strong connections? His comment seems to privilege the signified and assumes a transparency between the sign and the referent (what I was originally referring to as the signifier and the signified and which, I am realizing, is a common replacement in poststructural discussions of signification—perhaps what Barthes would call a connotation of signification . . .)

I am going to hunt up that de Certeau citation and read on.

Postscript: What about writing itself as a colonizing activity? We organize the spaces of our perceived landscapes, and just as they moved buildings from London/Paris to Cairo (and Cairo to Paris: the obelisk), we do the same by taking words from others (especially the continental philosophers) and rebuilding them word for word on our pages; organizing space on the pages to reflect what we see as a controlled, grid-like pattern or linearity in order to make our statements about whatever . . . Seeing the task as one of getting rid of the "chaotic" in the colonized spaces of writing books.

Post-postscript: Though even these somewhat chaotic pages of mine have been organized to object to typical organized patterns. Such antlike creatures we are, stuck in our colonies, doomed to colonize or be colonized.

Post-post-postscript: But maybe Derek was referring to the notion of landscape as a view—as one particular text of representation?

—readers are travellers; they move across lands belonging to someone else, like nomads poaching their way across fields they did not write . . .
Michel de Certeau (174)

strategies of representation that treat discourse as an unproblematic reflection of the world;" a critical human geography must move away from a spatial science that imposes "estrangement on people, places, and landscapes;" and it must include an examination of what is done in the name of geography, in order to "make human life not only intelligible, but better" (75, 76).

Following a general overview[24] of how geography has evolved to where it is today, I would like to consider developments related to poetics and bodies, two areas I believe relate directly to each other and to the above tenets put forth by Derek Gregory.

While universities received their impetus for raising the status of geography from schoolteachers, once geography became established as a university discipline, it became more and more specialized and intellectual and rigorous, and began to move away from school geography, which had become by the 1950s, a study of regional focus. This regional focus was apparent within academic geography during the same time period. Following the regional focus within human geography, a focus which concentrated on physical aspects of regions, the 1960s was the decade of the "new geography."

This new geography presented the discipline as quantitative, as a spatial science. Peter Haggett's work is within this particular conception of geography. His book *The Geographer's Art* (published in 1990 and reprinted in 1995, indicating that spatial science geographers continue to play a role in present-day academic geography), describes geography as a mirror of the world and examines how "geographers have polished and adjusted their mirrors to get particular images of the world around them" (19). This conception of geography is an example of Ted Aoki's imaginary Discourse A, and the semiotic equation where world is privileged, where language is assumed to reflect the world, and where writing is conceived of as writing *about* the world.

Following a decade of spatial science, the 1970s were a time for reversal, for rejection of positivism and a move to considering more of the human in human geography. Engagement with social theory and a good deal of cross-disciplinary mingling during this decade (for example, a mingling of economics, sociology, and anthropology) led to a radical geography. Projects (writing and research) within this radical geography were concerned with experience and the life-world and included a questioning of grand theory. Civil rights, social justice, and Marxist theory were influential during this time. An example of this more radical turn within human geography is work by David Ley on social movements and neighborhood struggles. It was also during this decade that feminist geography arose out of an initial reaction to the absence of women within the discipline.

This radical geography continued to evolve through the 1980s and developed into a more critical geography. Referring to the critical aspect of current academic geography, Felix Driver notes that "many geographers are now writing confidently and expansively about the history and current condition of their own discipline" and in so doing, these geographers are not just trying to justify their own discipline, but rather to "offer new perspectives on geographical inquiry" (97–98).

Closer engagement with social theory added to this critical aspect of geography. During the late 1980s and early 1990s, Derek Gregory identifies "an explosion of interest in 'culture' across the spectrum of the humanities and the social sciences," and another "new" geography evolved—the "new cultural geography" (133). The two main themes that appear within this recent academic geographical landscape are the increased engagement with social theory and its intersections with human geography and, closely related, the attention to place, space, and landscape within this "socialized" human geography (4). A look at the back covers of recent publications illustrates the interdisciplinary rhizomatic traveling that is happening within human geography. Publishers are cross-referencing books published within human geography as also in the categories of gender studies, sociology, cultural studies, women's studies, literature, cartography, and cultural geography.

An important development within human geography is the recognition of geography as a discourse. Derek Gregory speaks of his writings regarding geographical imaginations as "interventions in a discourse rather than a discipline" (3). The notion of geography as a discourse is a recognition that what we do and say and write regarding geography is all part of what geography is (becoming). It is not a static body of knowledge. Geography is constituted through discursive practices; and this is the notion of poetics—our words do not mime the world, rather, they intervene in the world (becoming); and this is the notion of the line dance.

* *

Cool Memories and Dreams IV
Curricular Re-Visions

The following statements will appear in the new curriculum:

• It is important to recognize that the subject of geography is a socially constructed entity (a body of knowledge constructed by bodies), and as such, is open to re-vision and change.

• A discourse constitutes the ways we think and speak and write about geography in our everyday living, as well as the skills and tools we use in our negotiations of space, place and landscape. How we write and speak and study geography (the discursive practices) is just as important to investigate as its content. Geography is moving away from a spatial sciences emphasis, prevalent in the 1960s, into a consideration of broader social theory. Curricular documents are endeavoring to incorporate more recent perspectives regarding geography as a discourse.

• While map skills will continue to be a component within school geography, this approach needs to be balanced out with analysis and critique of the uses and abuses of maps in society. It is recommended that students at all grade levels be exposed to the historical traditions of geography and of mapping.

• The environmental determinism perspective that promoted the "physical environment" as determining settlement patterns, movement, and exploration needs to be replaced by a critical social theory that recognizes the role of power, knowledge, and human agency in settlement patterns, movement, and exploration.

• A language of systems and management has been associated with geography. Teachers and students are encouraged to consider the results of this form of technical, indifferent language in relation to our world and our place within the world. Poetic language . . .

* *

The present decade has seen a continued broadening of human geography to encompass postmodernist, feminist, poststructuralist, and more recently, postcolonialist perspectives. What I have to offer you on the following pages is a collection of post-cards—highlights of major attractions. These post-cards are from texts within the present academic landscape of human geography, where geography is critiqued and examined for the way it has been constructed. In particular, current writing and research in academic geography calls into question the language and writing practices that exist within geography and that have gone unnoticed in the past, and how these practices influence our thinking and living in the worlds we write and read (the notion of poetics here). Several texts attend to embodied geo-graphying.

Post-Cards

> ### Writing Worlds: Discourse, Text and Metaphor in the Representation of Landscape
> (Trevor Barnes and James Duncan)
>
> Trevor Barnes and James Duncan consider poststructural perspectives regarding texts and representations of landscape, noting that "in spite of the fact that human geographers write for a living, until recently the actual process of writing was considered unproblematic" (1). These two earth-writers discard the imaginary Discourse A that privileges world and move into the space of Discourse B, privileging words and the space between words; adhering to the notion that the word is the world (or the space of difference between words and texts is the world). They note that writing "is constitutive, not simply reflective; new worlds are made out of old texts, and old worlds are the basis of new texts" (3). Such activities as "drawing maps, making plans, and even painting" (5) are considered by these authors to be textual representations of landscape. From there they move to the poststructural perspective á la Roland Barthes that every reading of these written texts involves a rewriting.

Deconstructing the Map
(J.B. Harley)

One result of this close attention to the problematics of writing within human geography (including writing/reading maps) is a close reading and deconstruction of maps. Works by several writers in human geography question the relationship between map and territory, and the relationships between mapmakers and maps/territories and map-readers. J.B. Harley notes that accepting texts as intertextual opens a space for reading maps to uncover "alternative" and "competing" discourses. He contends that maps are about texts and knowledge and power. Harley lists as examples of the colonial power of maps the way Europeans were able to "draw lines across the territories of Indian nations without sensing the reality of their political identity," and the pin and paper map battles that generals have been able to fight, totally removed from the bloody battlefields. He notes that "while the map is never the reality, in such ways it *helps* to create a different reality" (247). (Emphasis added. His word "helps" makes his statement sound a bit like ". . . the map is the territory is the . . .")

Designs on Signs/Myth and Meaning in Maps
(Denis Wood and John Fels)

Subscribing to Roland Barthes's notions of denotation and connotation, Denis Wood and John Fels examine maps for their myths and meanings. They read a North Carolina state highway map and they remind us that "there is nothing natural about a map. It is a cultural artifact, an accumulation of choices made among choices every one of which reveals a value" (65), even though a map is typically assumed to be neutral and nonpolitical, especially a tourist map like the state highway map of North Carolina. They note that county borders on this highway map run right through Indian reservation land, indicative of the role of the map in "pretending to be neutral on an issue over which people are divided" (64). Woods and Fels claim that most maps are used to possess, claim, legitimate, and name (71).

****
Cool Memories and Dreams V
A Classroom

Social Studies Curricular Focus:
- map skills
- critical thinking
- questioning and challenging in the process of informed decision making
- including multiple perspectives
- making connections between past, present, and future

Activity 1:
The mapping tradition is associated with colonial, imperialistic power and authority and was generally undertaken by male explorers. Encourage students to explore the way geography has been constructed. Students might examine reasons for mapping in colonial times and in postcolonial times, various cultures and their mapping traditions, why maps change, how maps appear in popular culture, and the hidden messages in maps. Consider how you might make the familiar strange by taking a poststructural approach to reading maps.

Activity 2:
As an introduction to the place of maps in our everyday lives, ask students to collect objects that depict maps and cartographic images as decoration (greeting cards, gift wrap, clothing). Have students look for advertising that uses these same images. Several interesting patterns will emerge regarding how maps are associated with authority, power, and gender in our everyday, pop-culture lives.

****

Space and Social Theory
(Georges Benko and Ulf Strohmayer)

In their edited collection of essays regarding space and social theory, Georges Benko and Ulf Strohmayer note the fragmentation of geographic approaches within human geography that arose out of the postmodern turn. Their collection of essays is a cross-section of several approaches to postmodernity evident within research and writing, and these authors openly admit and even celebrate the fact that these approaches are conflicting and contrasting and create anything but "harmonious discourse." Text and author, modernity vs. postmodernity or even hypermodernity, and defining and redefining identities within spatial considerations are just some of the issues featured in this collection.

Hypermodernity, Identity, and the Montage Form
(Allan Pred)

In relation to textual practices, Allan Pred breaks away from the linear narrative in his montage essay, and while he is writing about hypermodernity/postmodernity, his writing form performs the fragmentation and intersplicing of these same two concepts. He notes that montage has been described as "creative geography" by Soviet filmmaker Lev Kuleshov (138). Pred asks:

How may we (re)constructively re-present the present,
creatively produce on-the-page images
of our mental images and reflective reworkings
   of the contemporary world(s)
      in which our everyday lives are interwoven . . . ? (119)

Progress in Geography and Gender. Or Something Else
(Gillian Rose)

Some of the strongest questioning and critique of the discipline of geography, and language more specifically, comes from feminist geographers. Gillian Rose believes that feminist geography "cannot be ignored" and that it is "at the heart of debates about this thing called geography" (535). Feminist geography covers a diverse range of topics and includes a rich source of literature in research journals. Research projects situated within feminist geography examine such varied issues as the effects of household chores on the geographical location of women's waged work, safe spaces in urban areas for women, women's lives and spatial restrictions, and gendered experiences regarding body size, image, and clothing choices of people working in banks and other financial institutions.

Other Figures in Other Places: On Feminism, Postmodernism and Geography
(Liz Bondi)

Regarding texts and writing practices in the production of geographical knowledge, Liz Bondi points out that it has been widely assumed that "language is a medium through which knowledge can be unproblematically represented and transmitted. Language is viewed as transparent, its active role in shaping discourse is denied" (204). Feminist geographers dispute the transparency of language and attempt to illustrate the power and politics of language, recognizing that how we write about geographical knowledge determines our understandings of geographical knowledge. Feminist geography supports alternate linguistic forms of writing besides the "formal language of science, supposedly bereft of ambiguity, passion and so on and produced primarily by men and frequently defined in opposition to feminine linguistic forms" (204). Within a feminist geography perspective, such forms of discourse as poetry, drama, personal anecdote, and narrative accounts hold possibilities for transmitting and shaping geographical knowledge and geography itself as a discourse/discipline.

Remapping the Body/Land: New Cartographies of Identity, Gender, and Landscape in Ireland

(Catherine Nash)

Postmodern, feminist, and postcolonialist perspectives within human geography attempt to get back the body by acknowledging, and often privileging, the local, the personal, the situated nature of our lives. These perspectives actually point out that even in the disembodied viewing, the body is often present in the form of the landscape. Landscape is often equated with a woman's body, an essentialized, close-to-nature, maternal body in some cases, and in others, a mysterious, exotic, wild body that must be known and tamed. Catherine Nash looks at issues of gender and national identity within the Irish "landscape." She highlights how the act of naming and the act of mapping have the power of representation. She uses the artwork of Kathy Prendergrast (volcanic mountains as breasts, deserts as bellies, vulvas as passages) to "write back," and to remap, the appropriation of Irish culture and the gendering of landscape and nation within Ireland (227–250).

Re:Mapping Subjectivity

(Kathleen Kirby)

In her contributing chapter to the edited collection *BodySpace*, Kathleen Kirby discusses the way maps separate subjects and space, and how they also present a mediating space between subjects and space. She suggests that there is a gender differential in spatial negotiation; that men somehow are accustomed to erasing their physicality (52) and that women do not have the same luxury; as well, men are more accustomed to taking on a removed, distancing view, whereas women are more immersed in their surroundings. She believes that mapping has excluded ways of negotiating space that take into account ground-level perspectives and the lived everyday of bodies in spaces. She is hopeful for inclusive transformations to mapping, even though they may require "eradicating, radically, the ordering lines of our culture and our selves" (55).

The Power of Disembodied Imagination: Perspective's Role in Cartography

(Ken Hillis)

Ken Hillis describes how perspective-taking requires a disembodied positioning. That is, if we imagine ourselves actually able to view the territory we are viewing within a map text, it becomes necessary to detach from our bodies. While this only happens at the subconscious level, Hillis shows through the use of diagrams of perspective and view (and a very dense text) that disembodied (literally a head with no body) is the only way we can possibly view a map—we do not even realize that in our subconscious imaginations we have severed our bodies from our heads (or perhaps our eye from our body) in order to take in the view. He notes: "In detaching vision from embodiment we too are diminished, our left-behind bodies marginalized, as is that which lies beyond perspectives horizon. This is one reason why it becomes easier for the eye to venture forth. The body that would hold it in place has been reduced to insignificance" (13). Like Hillis, my desire for a more embodied geo-graphying is because I "understand the material body, eyes included, to form the basis or actuality of geographic experience from which we negotiate ongoing and intersubjective relationship[s]" (15). [25]

Another Borderland

So, then, after traveling through the landscapes of academic geography and curricular geography, what now can I say about curricular geography and desires for poetic possibilities and embodied knowing?

In general, I noted that geography was constructed within the planned lines of curriculum in the following ways:

• as a set of concepts that were considered to be geographical and as such were set apart for particular units of study. This set of concepts was dependent on a view of geography as a discipline, a body of knowledge, rather than a discourse.

• as a set of tools and skills that were necessary for the geographically literate person, and in order to manage the earth (removed from the world, managing the world).

• as a set of two separate geographies related and connected to each other: physical geography and human geography. (Out of a blindness to how geography itself is a human construction, we have created the split between physical and human. Perhaps this has led to a need to manage and control the world.)

* *

Cool Memories and Dreams VI
Teacher Education Assignment

Study #1:
Within your study group, read the following two selections:

1. Richard Henley's chapter from *Language and Learning in the Teaching of Geography*: "The Ideology of Geographical Language" (pp. 162–171).

2. The following pages from the unit "Identity" in the Grade 4 Saskatchewan Social Studies Curriculum Guide: pp. 103–118. (The focus of this particular unit is on the following geographical concepts listed on page 104: regions and their definition; population distribution; relationships between/among climate, landforms, vegetation, population distribution, opportunities for work, rural/urban communities in Saskatchewan.)

Poetic considerations for discussion:
• How is the world being written within this unit of study? (What observations can you make regarding the wider social and economic climate and the dominant ideological formations within the context of this unit?)

• How could we, in classrooms, interrupt this writing?

• Should we?

"For obvious reasons linguistic questions are of interest to all those, including historians, philologists and others, who need to deal with texts. Even more obvious is the importance of linguistics for culture in general. In the lives of individuals and of societies, language is a factor of greater importance than any other." (Saussure 7)

* *

I noted that geography was written in "physical" terms—features of landscape, regions, map skills, location finding, distribution of resources and people, size and structure.

If we considered geography as a rhizomatic discourse in our planning lines, rather than as a tree of knowledge discipline (Gregory *x*), there are possibilities for making sense of our everyday places and spaces within a study of the major concepts included within social studies; for example, considering how we might graphy the geo and our place within it through an examination of culture, conflict, change, values, needs, power, decision making, and so on. These possibilities further multiply if we apply the components of the landscape of social studies education (see Figure 1) to the teaching and learning of geography.

While geographical concepts are currently located within social studies education, and a skills orientation is promoted with regard to geography, we do not appear to consider how we might approach these same concepts within the landscape of social studies education in "social studies" ways. Poetic possibilities become present if we encourage critical thinking, including multiple perspectives, making connections between past, present, and future, and honoring and respecting self and others while we try to make sense of space and place in our everyday living (and here I borrow from Derek Gregory's very general, rhizomatic description of geography).

Throughout my wanderings, it appeared that geography itself as a construction[26] was not overtly discussed in any of these curricular documents. Rather, geography was something that just "is." There was no consideration of theories of geography. There was no inquiry into the "lack of innocence in any discourse" (geography included) "by looking at the textual staging of knowledge and the effects of language on giving meaning to experience" (Lather 120).

The line dancing that happens in signification was not acknowledged. Geography curriculum has not attended to deconstructive practices or critical reflection regarding textual practices at all. Surely, within a social science these topics should be attended to. We need to be encouraging students to inquire into language and texts in geography, to inquire into both the methods and the content that is considered geography, to inquire into the discursive practices.

And what, you might be asking, does this have to do with line dancing? Well, remember the part about world, word, and we and the dance between? It is very important to consider how we write the world of geography education, and how this in turn writes the world in certain ways, and writes us within that world in certain ways. Word can include curricular documents. How we study about the world is also a writing of the world, and if we study the world in detached, disembodied ways, we risk alienating ourselves and others from the world. Remember, curriculum is about self and world. Curricular decisions need to consider how we might manage and solve the problems of the world, as well as how we might live and learn in the world and create our worlds as we live and write.

Throughout my curricular travels, it appeared to me that world was privileged or was attributed a considerable amount of metaphysicalness in the way geography teaching and learning were arranged. It seemed like a case of "Here is the world—learn its lines, and manage and use the world in sustainable ways." On the other hand, there was also a certain amount of privileging the word as written. There was not a lot of evidence in my travels that our words and worlds perform wor(l)des.

The spatial science era of the 1960s has lingered within curricular geography to the present day; and this lingering has been at the expense of a more human approach to the study of geography. Within social studies, geographical concepts seem to be the place where we detach from the lived world and disembodied study is encouraged. Poetic possibilities open up if we first of all reconsider our definition of geography. Possibilities for embodied knowledge open up if we consider geography as a discourse, rather than a discipline, and a discourse that actually crosses traditional subject boundaries. Rather than ending geography lessons with locating our places, and learning the lines about our places, a discursive, rhizomatic construction of curricular geography might make it easier to continue on with "geography" or "social studies" as we write or read poetry or creatively write lines about spaces and places instead of waiting to do this after moving on into "language arts" period.[27]

In my curricular travels, I did not note any direct references to current research or writing located within "academic geography," and vice versa. While I did note several references pertaining to *Journal of Geography* within teacher education textbooks, there were no references to journals[28] such as *Progress in Human Geography*; *Environment and Planning*; *Gender, Place and Culture: A Journal of Feminist Geography*; *Geography*; or the *New Zealand Journal of Geography*. Curricular geography needs to be more rhizomatic, making connections and crossing spaces that have not been crossed enough in the past.

Attending to the current cultural/social theory focus within academic geography and to the discipline's self-conscious critique of itself would highlight the poetics of geography and would lead to an acknowledgment and encouragement of including embodied knowing within curricular geography. Taking its cue from academic geography, curricular geography (I mean here, teacher educators, curriculum developers, and classroom teachers) must begin to question the what and how of geography and move toward an inclusion of more personal geography-ing within our study of geography, an awareness of the sociotextual act of teaching geography, and a more material notion of "bodies" of knowledge.

The current detached, disembodied approach within school geography has received little attention. While geography is usually split between physical and human systems, and recent rec-ommendations call for more emphasis on the human side, even this human side to geography is referred to in *systems* language. Concerned with power and justice and the ideological attributes of language, Richard Henley (writing about British school geography) notes how the language of school geography is ideologically loaded, and in its use, creates a "flattening of reality" (166). The world is written in a language of indifference. School geography is still heavily influenced by a spatial sciences perspective, and if we believe Elspeth Deir, it will become even more and more a technological study of digital analysis. Also, the heavy concentration on map skills within school geography leads to a detached writing of the world.

It strikes me that what is at the heart of the debate within geography as an academic discipline appears to remain, at best, on the margins of debates regarding school geography. My travels into the curricular landscape of school geography yielded no direct references to feminist geography (although I believe parallels do exist between the basic tenets of feminist geography and social studies education).[29] Australia and New Zealand are closer to the heart regarding feminist geography perspectives. A recent Australian study explores gender and literacy within the context of geography curriculum and cites feminist geography perspectives as informing the research and findings.[30] Writing in 1993, Robyn Longhurst and Robin Peace, two New Zealand academic geography scholars, admitted that while feminist geography was not yet being taught in New Zealand schools, the time was right for transferring those perspectives from the lecture theater into high school classrooms. The conversation at least is underway in those locations.

****

Cool Memories and Dreams VII
Course Proposal Draft

Title of Proposed Course: Geography and Curriculum
(ESST 315, Teacher Education)

General Purpose: The purpose of this course will be to provide an overview of the evolution of geography as a subject area (within both academic and curricular contexts), its location within social studies education, and how the major geographical themes of space, place, and landscape occur within present curriculum. This course will examine current trends and issues within the academic discipline of human geography, and will provide a forum for consideration and discussion regarding how these issues might inform geography curriculum in classrooms (K–12).

The course will focus on the role of language and discourse in shaping our understandings of the world that we study in geography classes (and how the way we study geography plays an important role in our understandings of geography); the notion of geography itself as a set of discursive practices; and how/why we might encourage embodied knowing within our study of geography.

Describe the Need/Impetus for the Proposed Course: While the current curricular milieu views social studies as an interdisciplinary approach/subject that includes geography as one of its disciplines, geography (making sense of space, place, and landscape in our everyday lives) is a major component. This course will provide those students who wish to specialize in social studies education (whether at the elementary or secondary level) with further opportunities to consider curriculum and instructional approaches in the teaching of school geography. Students would elect to take this course during the final year of their elementary education program, or within the curriculum year of their secondary education program. A summer course offering would also welcome returning classroom teachers.

Topics to Be Addressed:
• Geography as a curricular area

- Critical examination of curricular approaches with particular attention to language
- Geography as a discipline and a discourse
- Current trends and issues within academic geography
- The poetics of geography curricula
- Poetic approaches within the teaching of geography

Major Term Assignment Choices:
- Compilation of a Personal Atlas or Community Atlas

- Compilation of a Resource File related to one particular geographical theme (e.g., local community, map study, community comparison, spiritual geography, urban study, rural study, changing spaces, a field study, etc.)

- Presentation at the Social Studies Subject Council Conference or a submission to one of the listed journals

Short-Term Assignment Choices:
- Literature and landscape, poetry and place: compilation of poetry and literature that focuses on a particular geographical area that is studied at a particular grade level

- Critique of a journal article that focuses on the academic discipline, and relating this reading to curricular geography

- Critique of various instructional materials

Grading: Evaluation will be on a pass/fail system, the criteria for these two categories to be established by the students and instructor, with the instructor to have the final say in matters of discrepancy.

Note: It is possible that the responsibility for instructing this course could be shared in a collaborative approach by the Faculty of Arts and the Faculty of Education. A similar course offering is being considered within the Geography Department as an elective.

* *

CHAPTER THREE
POETIC POSSIBILITIES

oh how i have lived
the lines and spaces
on the maps
of these territories . . .

Poetics as an Active Composing/Imposing

When I ask about an instant in time/space when word becomes world becomes word, my curiosity centers on the relationship between our words and our worlds. In my search for poetic possibilities I want to consider *poetic* as an active composing/imposing of lines, as well as one way of composing/imposing lines (poetic language) within geography curriculum. I am asking, "What is the relationship between our words and our worlds? What do our words have to do with our worlds, and vice versa?" These are questions about what it means to take up a pen and write (literally and metaphorically speaking), to language (in the verb sense), to engage (either producing or processing, reading/writing) with a text[31]—text as "cultural practices of signification rather than as referential duplications" (Barnes and Duncan 5).

What is transpiring in the act of signification, in geography or any other discipline/discourse? When we take up a pen and write about our world, or read what has been written about our world, there is a preposition being erased in the process. The word "about" is erased. When we write or read about a place or an event, the words also play a role in shaping that place or event. And here is where lines dance—in the erasure of the preposition. This is text as performing.

So then, what does all this have to do with poetic possibilities in geo-graphy curriculum? If we attend to the relationship between word, world, and we that is inherent in semiotic equations, especially in the notion of wor(l)de, then we can take advantage of this space as a space for writing the world in active, creative ways. The performative space is there already. Perhaps it is more a case that we have not been recognizing the possibilities within this space. The poetic dance is always already happening.

Consider the geographical concept of "place." Along with literary and scientific descriptions of place, there is an aspect of writing that allows more than description of a place. In the writing, we imagine, and we create our places and lives. Several contemporary writers story landscapes and people.[32] Their narratives go beyond mere descriptions of place. Through their story and verse, these writers actively construct places (and selves). Wayson Choy, a Vancouver-born writer, notes how places also construct selves in his essay "The Ten Thousand Things": "At home, I turn on my computer to begin tapping out the second novel; in the middle of a sentence—like this one, in fact—I laugh aloud. I had been writing fiction about life in Chinatown; Chinatown, all these years, had been writing me" (22). And here is the word/world/we line dancing.

Reading/Writing Lines Poetically and Poststructurally

Even the lines that have already been written can be rewritten as we read them. It is possible to read poetically. To compose/impose our own lines within the lines we read/write. Take, for example, geographical and cartographical lines. A great deal of emphasis is placed within geography and social studies curriculum documents on map skills—reading and interpreting maps. When referring to making sense of maps, we say we "read" maps. But often our reading of maps ignores the narrative or writerly qualities of the map and we focus on the "facts." In this approach to reading maps, we read the text of the map as a closed text.

The facts presented on a map (population, land use, natural vegetation) are part of a grand narrative (for example, a narrative of capitalist economies, patriarchal societies, colonization, and "progress") of the space represented, and these grand narratives go largely unacknowledged in our everyday map "reading." We ignore the fact that maps tell us not only about the spaces; they also say just as much about the mapmakers and the culture that produced the space and the map. Not only are the grand narratives ignored, but our local everyday lived narratives of the space remain hidden among the lines,

Travel Notes

Place: Richmond

Supper with Pat. Fried Chicken. Crispy Strips and Crispy Fries (Pat's with gravy) eaten in front seat of car with interior light on. Very hungry. Read Pat's proposal draft while eating and talking. Traveling in the front seat with her notions of traveling theory.

Heard Carl Leggo speak on performativity. The performativity of language? Made me wonder about language as performance, and language as production. Tonight someone mentioned the similarity of performance and production.

I asked Ted Aoki about performance and production. Seems to me that I am not a part of the production when language is referred to as production—as producing reality/meaning. But language as performance includes me as a part of the performance. Ted noted the word "form" in performance, transformation, hmm. Conform? Informing? Anyway I do wonder about language as performance. Just what is performing? What is forming?

Good company on a journey
makes the way seem the shorter
                Izaak Walton

Place: Geography and Cartography and the Space Between

While cartography and geography are separate sciences, they are also closely related. Regarding the relationship between cartography and geography, Peter Haggett states that "maps play a distinctly more prominent and central role in geography than in other disciplines. No other insists that students include courses on map making, map reading, map projections and the like in their core curriculum" (8). As my travels through curricular landscapes indicate, this same focus on maps is evident within curricular materials in geography/social studies education.

I have not seen the need to differentiate between geography and cartography within this atlas. They are closely related within curricular planning and within living. In fact, geo/carto/auto/biography is a metonymic word for some of the writing that is included within this atlas. Each is related to the other, in an "and/not and" relationship. Cartography and autobiography are very much a part of geography.

From a spatial science perspective:

For if science is the art of the soluble, then much of geography is the art of the mappable.
                    Peter Haggett (6)

dots, and colors of the map.

A postmodern approach to narrative challenges the authority of grand narratives and recognizes the value of lived, everyday experiences and situated knowledges and narratives. While I do not see such a separation between grand narrative and local narrative, I do believe that reading maps in a way that allows a mingling of the grand narrative of a space with the local, lived narrative of that same space would enhance our notions of the space (or place), and ultimately our notions of ourselves.

There are connections between maps and narratives, whether or not the narrative form has been intentionally applied by the mapmaker/writer. Often when narrative is discussed, the writer of the narrative and the written text on the page are privileged in the discussion, over the reader of the narrative and the text as it is read. Rather than privilege the writer of narrative (we often focus on the author's intent), I would like to look at the narrative component often left out of discussions around narrative—the reader.

While a text might not be written with postmodern intentions (questioning the author, locating multiple centers . . .), the reader might still want to read the text in a postmodern way. I am suggesting that it may be in the reading of maps that the greatest possibilities for poetics are present. Barthes was one poststructuralist scholar who considered the reader as part of the narrative. That is, an author writes a text, it is there on the page, and as the reader reads the text, it becomes text-as-reading (*The Rustle of Language* 30). In effect, the act of reading the text is an act of writing as well. Barthes describes a writerly text as one that is open, a text that leaves room for the reader to write personal meaning into the text as it is being read. Nadine Gordimer argues that every reading is a writerly reading, regardless of the writer's intent, that is, every reader brings into a reading personal meaning and cultural signifiers, thus "writing" the text as it is being read (17).

It is this writerly reading that I want to explore in terms of reading maps. While it might be the case that every reading is writerly, what seems to be overlooked is the reader. Is every reader aware of the writerly aspects of reading, or cognizant of the possibilities of a writerly reading of text? I think this writerly reading is covert, and we have become accustomed to reading a text in author-itative ways; that is, we try to read the author's intent, while ignoring the differences in

Travel Notes

Place: Kootenay School of Writing

Ann Lauterbach, a member of the New York group of "language poets," was reading from her books of poetry. Very interesting poetry. And she was using her hand to gesture as she read phrases, sort of looked like she was gently tossing out words, rolling them out like dice with her hand as she read. Her poems were fragments strung together around events. Like the poem about the fires in Oakland, California. Her words were very descriptive and called forth images and feelings of lives and artifacts going up in smoke and sifting down like ashes around the observers. I spoke with her at the intermission and told her I enjoyed the poetic phrases, but often was behind her a couple of phrases, because I was so accustomed to trying to connect the fragments into some sort of narrative. I asked her if she was aware of listeners doing this as she read. She said she was and acknowledged that meaning-making was happening among the listeners. She had no control over that. She was attempting to disrupt notions of lyric, and write the everyday, fragmented as it is. She said that young people take to her poetry and her agenda very quickly. (Maybe because of their video lives?)

Even though Ann's poems are fragments strung together (contiguous?), they are beautiful pieces of the world. I especially liked the pieces she read from her book *And for Example.*

> *standing at the window*
> *watching space bend in the wind's fabric*
> *breaching the wave's hump*
>
> Ann Lauterbach (46)

the text. The differences between the author's lines and our lived lines.

Barthes describes writerly reading as that reading that occurs in the "looking up" space (*The Rustle of Language* 30). Writerly reading is a form of slow motion reading, wherein we bring our own meanings to the text as we read it. Concerning reading maps, it is this "looking up" space I would like to explore. The space not on the map, in the lines/text on the page. The space full of the differences between, the space that challenges the author/ity of the map text as it is being read. The space where the text-as-reading is written, where the space-as-lived is mapped. What would a reading of maps be like if we were to read in slow motion, to write in the local, lived everyday experiences of a place on the official map of that place? In the looking up space, what are the possibilities for inviting in a lived, local narrative of the spaces on the map? I think the possibility exists for the grand to mingle with the local, but only if we consciously allow this to happen. The reader of the map holds the creative power to author/ize or personalize the map and the narrative within the lines. In many respects, this approach to reading a map is much like reading between the lines—openly acknowledging personal narrative knowings of a place or difference in the text/lines of the space/map.

> All lines on a map, we must acknowledge, are imaginary; they are ideas of order imposed on the sloshing flood of time and space.
>
> Janette Turner Hospital (1)

A poetic reading of maps can be a disruptive reading of maps. That there might be empowering ways of reading a map disrupts the typical notion of how power is associated with representations of space. Power is usually associated with map making (the production of space), rather than map reading (the reading of space).

In an effort to disrupt the power of maps and mapping, a political group known as the Situationists International began a practice that David Pinder describes as subvertive cartography. This group of individuals developed a method of psychogeographical mapping to displace the authority of city maps and mapping. Psychogeographical mapping involved wandering through a city and getting a "feel" for the spaces that were mapped. In some cases, group members cut up city maps and created a collage of the different areas of the city, and then connected each cut-up section with arrows. The arrows indicated the direction of their travels. Engaging in psychogeographical mapping was how this group contested the "official" status of city maps. It was their attempt to "trace out how different forms of mapping, based on different values, desires, and needs that challenge the status quo can be developed" (406).

The geographies of everyday life were a concern of the Situationists International group. The notion of poetic reading is similar to psychogeographical mapping, and my concern is also with the geographies of everyday life. de Certeau describes an "anthropological, poetic and mythic experience of space," a space that is not evident on the maps (even of the Situationists) of city spaces and official spaces. Through a poetic reading of maps, the experience of space is acknowledged. I am not just concerned with city spaces, but with all of the spaces we live in and experience—country spaces, town spaces, café spaces, highway spaces, academic spaces, and the "spaces that cannot be seen" and whose paths "elude legibility" (93). As the map is read, the reader's personal meanings and knowings of that space can be acknowledged.

Reading maps is a very tactile experience. Who has not clutched a map to his or her bosom as security when confronted with new territory? Or sat hunched over the kitchen table, an index finger sensuously caressing or assertively pressing on the lines of the route to be followed on an impending journey (be it a local, continental, or more worldly destination). But beyond the tactile finger touching and map clutching in which I have taken part, and which I have witnessed, as we currently read maps we do not leave a space for embodied knowledge or readings of the spaces on the maps. Poetic reading makes a space for personal embodied ways of knowing the spaces on the maps of our places, and promotes a more empowered reading of maps.

Some modern-day maps are presented with several transparent overlays—additional information and reading made possible with each successive overlay. I thought I might be able to say what I want to say by using this same technique. An illustration of a poetic reading of space might be possible by starting with a map/space and then adding transparent levels to the surface reading of the map, each overlay being my writerly reading of how I have experienced the space on the map.

If we were to examine all of the possible layers of meaning and stories told in one map, while it might seem logical that the first level of meaning would come in the very act of mapping and the presence of maps in society, I think the story starts even before the map is in our hands, in the act of surveying a space. Many accounts of colonization describe the imperial travelers and explorers searching out a vantage point and surveying the land, observing from above, attempting a bird's-eye view from on high. Surveying the territory did not end with the visual. Official surveys, wherein land was divided up in geometrical fashion and survey stakes pounded in to pin down ownership and authority, actually authored the space before it was "written" on maps. Cadastral maps (those maps made to prove ownership and define boundaries) and commercial maps (those maps made to promote the travel and tourist industry and boost real estate sales) followed, and today the list of the ways a map is put to use is practically endless. And each of the uses of a map is a story; a grand narrative of people, cultures, and place.

The map itself is another layer of meaning, another chapter to the story of a space. What the lines enclose, the contents of the legend, the colors used, and the information not included all add to the detail of each level. The text-as-reading is another layer of meaning within the map. The text in the looking up spaces of the map, the text that is written while reading between the lines, holds narrative possibilities at the personal, local level.

I have put maps to various uses in my life thus far, most recently in the form of way-finding maps,[33] having moved from the prairies to the west coast. Maps have become necessary in my forays into the urban landscape, on freeways, side streets, transit lines, library floors, and shopping mall concourses. While the lines and symbols on the map often mystify a space, as I read the maps I am aware of the text-as-reading, that is, my own text of the places indicated on the map. My experiences of the place are added to the actual lines and symbols of the map, to reveal an intertextuality of the territory. As I read the text of the map, I am able to bring my own text to that reading, and this brings increased personal significance to the map. So the writing that occurs in the looking up space of the reading can be added to the text of the map.

I am not trying to say that maps are narratives and nothing else, or that we should only be concerned with one way of reading/writing maps. Rather, I am saying that if we think of maps as narratives of space, as well as statements of fact, and take part in a poetic reading of the space on the map, maps take on meanings at the level of local narrative as well as meanings at the level of grand narrative. A mingling of the grand narrative of a place or territory with the local, lived narrative of that same place is encouraged, and our notions of place and self are enhanced. In the case of reading space, we write our own local lived narratives between the lines on the map, as we pay attention to the "looking up" spaces, as we take part in spacious, poetic readings.

Reading space in a way that allows for a mingling of grand and local requires attending to "point of view," and in fact, changing our viewpoint. The panoptical view (God's-eye view) from above[34] must switch to a view from the ground level. Adrienne Rich writes a world in her book of poems, *An Atlas of the Difficult World.* Discarding the bird's-eye view, Rich comes down to ground level as she maps the "haunted river flowing from brow to groin" and the "desert where missiles are planted like corms." She declares: "I promised to show you a map you say but this is a mural / then yes let it be these are small distinctions / where do we see it from is the question" (6). On the following pages I present several "map-poems" as poetic possibilities for writing the world; for seeing it (and saying it) from a different vantage point. My poetic lines are written between, within, and on top of the lines already drawn on maps from my everyday living.

Some of these map-poems were originally produced with transparent overlays of poetic text, requiring readers (myself included) to place a fleshy hand between the layers in order to read the lines. Because of publishing formats for this atlas, the poems printed on the transparent layers were scanned onto the map images, eliminating the need (and cost) of the transparency. The map-poems contest the widely accepted bird's-eye view of maps and they attempt to bring the corporeal into map reading/writing. How I have lived the lines and spaces on the maps of these territories—whether rural, urban, or borderline spaces between countries—is explored within the lines of the following map-poems.

Poststructuralism blurs the boundary between reading and writing. As we read the lines that have already been written on maps, it is possible to live poetically within those lines; to rewrite the lines as we read; to impose/compose lines according to our own lived, bodily experiences.

LIVING A LANDSCAPE OF GEOMETRICAL PROGRESSION

　　warm
early summer evenings
the upstairs window open to the prairie breeze
my sisters already breathing their sleep breath
I listened to the traffic
　　living on an edge
inside an intersection
I heard travellers leaving town
sounding off into the depths
until the anticipated click
as they reached the point of intersection
where the railway tracks crossed the highway
　　upstairs in my bed
blowing over my face and body
a breeze so soft
the same breeze
that skimmed over the hood of the car
as it crossed the tracks
　　years later
still living inside an intersection
but on an opposite corner
on warm sunny afternoons
with my strollered baby
I leave the town behind
the prairie landscape a perfect study of perspective
lines moving off
in ever widening angles
I am always at the vertex
　　reaching the railroad tracks
I turn back toward town
welcoming the same breeze
that has blown
over my body
all these years

Map produced by Dale Shauf for the R.M. of Cambria #6

TRANSIT LINES

inside the Orange Line   Saturdays and Sundays between 10 a.m.
and 4 p.m.   the sign above me   **These Seats Reserved for
Persons Disabled and Seniors**   *forgive us our trespasses*   I   am
surrounded by **Seniors**   a woman sitting by the window says to the
man beside her: Are you wearing long underwear?

*yellowed, waffle-weave leg
sticking out of black fortrel trouser*

the man says he wears them for his arthritis and slaps his knee   she
says: Someone in here doesn't know when to stop with the perfume.
It's really rank. My mother used to say there's no need to use
perfume just make sure you wash   your body
real good   she gets off the bus
      alone   she says she'll sure be glad to get away
from the smelly perfume

two women sitting beside me start to talk: Do you notice the perfume?
No, I sure don't   they tell each other where they live one of the
women is holding something on her lap   she says: Look what I've
got in here   feel it   it's still warm

*a cup of soup
in a plastic margarine container
placed in a paper bag
inside of another clear plastic bread bag*

she tells about Sunday Seniors Lunch   she can take leftovers
home   the other woman pulls the cord to get off at
the next stop   she stands in the aisle   waiting
behind the yellow line   alone   the
woman with the soup says: Speak to me if you see me again

          and I'll do the same for you

Map image courtesy of Andreas Nothiger (Pocket Map Art)

LIVING IN LINEAR FASHION

When I was 19 I took a day trip with my grandmother.
We went to visit the relatives down

across. I stood with my great-grandmother at the end of
the day, waiting to leave, to make it back before the line
closed. In her shrunken body, my great-grandmother
stood straight beside me. Although the temperature was
still 31° Celsius (instantly converted into 95° Fahrenheit
when we crossed the line, like kilometers into miles, bags
into sacks, African Americans into Blacks, hillsides into
side hills, mickys into fifths) she was wearing gloves and
real nylons with seams. *Not those ridiculous pantyhose.*
Two stitched lines running down the backs of her legs
reminding me of blackened versions of lines of
albumen refusing to detach in the separation of egg
yolk from egg white. My great-grandmother told me to
just look at that: standing on the steps of the farmhouse,
her youngest daughter, whose 60 years of living left her
with a body the perfect antithesis of playtex invisible
lines of 18-hour control and cross-your-heart lift and
separation. *Oh, I wish she'd wear a girdle or something.*

When she was 96 my great-grandmother stopped
visiting her daughter who lived across the line 25 miles
away. She said she did not want to die in Canada. It
would be too much trouble to get her body home across
the line. Her last two years of living ran in parallels with
the 49th. Like the colouring books of my childhood,
long afternoons spent learning to colour within the lines,
we spend our lives learning to keep our bodies living
within the lines on the maps of our territories.

Travel Notes

Place: Desk

The thing is, we need to teach students that they can be geo-graphers. They can write their place and other places. Play with/in the lines and spaces of "official" geographical knowledge, facts, figures. Write their own atlas of their local places and other places. Human geography and space—space not just a mappable territory. Poetic function of language allows this to happen.

We need to attend to writing: creating, actively composing/imposing our world with our words. And reading in ways that also allow an imposing of words.

In the past we have not attended to the ways writing and words have shaped our understanding of the world and places in our geography lessons.

We need to notice this and look for possibilities here in how words can continue to write the world and bring embodied experiences into geography.

By taking an active role, our bodies become part of it, part of the writing.

Air they scarcely notice curls and rustles
each dry leaf, along, across
this inland sea. In shy experiments of touch
and part, they sail an unfamiliar coast, discovering.
                                        Bill New

Place: Desk

Something very interesting I recently read/wrote: "Performing Writing" by Della Pollock. It is an excellent chapter in the book *The Ends of Performance* and it outlines how writing can perform a form and a message at the same time. In the performing of a form, writing writes double messages on the page, or layers of meaning. Her discussion of metonymy is helpful. Maybe that is the thing about writing and language and being in the world, in a culture. Anything we say is always already what we don't say also, because of who we are and where we are. The backslash is imperative in metonymic writing. It is there anyway, even if we don't trace over it. For example, when we speak of language, we could write the word as: *language/culture*, but we don't, yet the two are part of each other—contiguity here? Same with word/world or wor(l)de; this is illustrative of metonymy.

The poem I wrote about women and families is performative writing. The words perform the form: montage, and the words perform a message about writing everyday living on a page, which, of course, montage form helps to portray, along with the words. It is still linear, because I do want control over my message. That is evident in the performance too; how we have imperialistic instincts, even over words.

Montage is transgression
　of the (hyper)modern condition(ing)s
　out of which it is created.
　　　　　　Allan Pred (137)

def•i•ni•tion*

wom•en and fam•i•lies
a group of words
meaning?
some days my
    is it gym today?

        he needs his inserts
                he is late again

        that damn dryer
thoughts
        I did not think he was   this fridge is full of
           his parents will not eat this

     they will hate the couch
           I should have gone to that meeting
              e-mail carbon copies
are so
           I did not know about her cancer
   what will she do for her cat
                    they really want a dog

fragmented
     why can't we have a dog
       a stage of not liking mothers
     sensitivity or
              I forget the coupon book every
        buy it anyway
    the grant application
it becomes
          how can I say this in 50 lines
       he needs a haircut
   we need a drive
   always something rolling rattling in the
difficult to
        she thinks she needs him
     he will take her money
            she should leave
make any
    a good idea for lunches
        how to keep it cold till

why won't she say it?
meaning seem clear
it's the dreaming

*the act or process of explaining or making clear the meaning of a word or group
of words[35]

Poetic as a Way of Composing/Imposing: Embodied Knowledge

> Moonlight, a cessation of clear, harsh day, is associated with mystery and illusive glimpses. The moon seems to have its own light, yet that light is reflected light, deriving from the sun which illuminates the everyday world. If, in the moonlight, we "handle" that muted radiance, there is no substance we are touching. We are playing with shadows made of darkness and reflected light. . . . When you read or write a poem you are handling moonlight.
>
> Margaret Demorest (364)

Handling moonlight. What more can I say? Except, of course, to ask, *Might there be places for handling moonlight within geography lessons?* (And perhaps we might even find that everything is moonlight—mystery and illusive glimpses.)

Poetry is a language that attempts to say what words cannot say. Poetry, in all its illusiveness, has the ability to affect us through our body, soul, and mind. Several philosophers who explore poetry make the connection between body and soul. Gaston Bachelard describes poetry as a phenomenology of the soul rather than one of the mind (*xxii*).

Poetry is a phenomenology of the body/mind/soul. Poetic language calls forth sensual experiences and rememberings, and poetic language has physiological effects on our bodies. Diane Ackerman explores how "sense-luscious" the world is, and notes the effect that language has on our bodies. She writes about the sound of poetry and its effects on our heartbeat, especially poetry written in iambic meter, which mimics a regular heartbeat—"ba-BUM, ba-BUM, ba-BUM: It locks up the heartbeat in a cage of words, and we, who respond so deeply to heart sounds, read the poem with our own pulse as a silent metronome" (180).

Noticing similar physiological effects of poetry (whether from reading it or writing it), Laurel Richardson reminds us that:

> An experiencing person is a person in a body. Poetry can recreate embodied speech in a way that standard sociological prose does not because poetry consciously employs such devices as line length, meter, cadence, speed, alliteration, assonance, connotation, rhyme and off-rhyme, variation and repetition to elicit bodily response in readers/listeners [and, I think writers]. . . . Poetry, built as it is on speech as an embodied activity, touches both the cognitive and the sensory in the speaker and the listener.
>
> Lived experience is lived in a body and poetic representation can touch us where we live, in our bodies. (26)

Anne Michaels tells us that "[t]he poem enters the body through the brain: it is a taste crushed open in the mouth as sound; vowels of light in our eyes; it summons bodily experience universal and yet intimate to each of us" (183).

Like Margaret Demorest, I see poetry as re-creating situations from the concrete external world, and at the same time "intent upon the opposite world: that of the abstract, invisible, interior world of feelings and insight experienced in that external world. . . . [P]oetry evolves from the private and lonely and unutterable world of the individual's emotions" (360).

"The world is more wonderful than any of us have dared to guess, as all great poets have been telling us since the invention of poetry" (Sharon Butala 56). In her discussion of a spiritual geo-graphy, Sharon Butala credits poetry with the ability to speak of spiritual knowings about our places. Thomas Moore points to poetry as a way of re-enchanting the world—of attending to the particularities of our everyday places. He suggests that poets or "perhaps any of us living with imagination" are the "transparence of place when the spirit of our ground concretely influences what we do and the way we live" (152). Poetic language, then, makes a space for embodied knowledge in our reading/writing of the wor(l)de.

A space
> *: to get messy with our places*
> *: to welcome the breezes that blow across our faces*
> *: to speak of the dryness on our lips*
>> *and in our breath*
>> *when we live on the prairies:*
>>> *a dryness not noticed*
>>> *until, living with wetness*
>>> *its presence is recognized*
>>> *in its absence*

Embodied knowings of places would mean attending to the smells, tastes, touches, intuitions, and emotions that we associate with a place. Kathleen Kirby recognizes a gender differentiation in spatial neg-otiation, and she posits that embodied knowing of a place has not been included in traditional ways of mapping spaces and places because of a need to distance oneself from the place being studied. She believes that people have been alienated from their environments because of a scientific requirement to be at an "objective distance from the phenomena [being analyzed]" (51).[36] Rather than standing back and observing a place from a removed vantage point, embodied knowing requires getting messy with the spaces—living the spaces, celebrating embodied spaces, even in our writing/reading. "Our task is that of taking up the written word, with all of its potency, and patiently, carefully, writing language back into the land" (Abram 272–273).

Back in 1916, John Dewey wrote about schools as places for uniting body, mind, and soul, and the relationship of intellect and emotions in theories of knowledge (335–337). Yet it is only in recent years that embodied ways of knowing, somatic knowing, have entered epistemological discussions within education and curriculum theory. While modernity has required an objective separation of mind and body, feminist and postmodern epistemologies recognize the impossibility of separating mind from body (embodied minds, mindful bodies). Traditional learning theories are based on a continuum that moves from the more concrete to abstract reasoning, yet it is now recognized that disembodied abstract reasoning is not distinctly separate from an embodied, sensual knowing. The senses of sight, touch, hearing, smell, taste, intuition, and emotion inform our rational knowing, and vice versa.

In a recent publication in the field of educational research, several established scholars describe mind-body connections that have been evident in their researching lives. They speak of an "entire dimension of experience" (Heshusius and Ballard xiii), personal, embodied ways of knowing, that has been left out of the research project, and of the possibilities found in narrative inquiry for exposing and celebrating mind-body connections. Referring to spiritual knowing, Butala says the same thing: "A whole, valuable dimension of human experience remains unsung and unvalidated" (55), and she blames this silence on our subscription to a scientific approach to knowing the world. My attempt in this discussion of accountable knowledge is not to refute the value of objective, disembodied knowing, but rather to include embodied ways of knowing alongside or within or surrounding objective, detached knowing.

When I think of curriculum and epistemological considerations, several possible reasons for the absence or ignorance of embodied and spiritual knowings of place come to mind. Patriarchal frameworks for knowledge and curriculum permeate the institution of education.

Embodied, personal knowing and narrative knowing have been associated with women and children within the project of modernity. Lyotard credits modernity with the scientific view that narratives are "savage, primitive, underdeveloped, backward, alienated, composed of opinions, customs, authority, prejudice, ignorance, ideology. . . fables, myths, legends, fit only for women and children" (27).

The Platonic tradition of debate, with its arguments and statements of claims, so embedded in modern educational institutions, ignores emotions, intuitions, and bodily knowings; these phenomena are traditionally associated with the feminine. I can recall being told to deny my emotions and intuitive knowings in the very early stages of my own teacher education program (*don't take things personally*), and in present-day schools and classrooms, teachers are cautioned about bodily contact with their students. Bodies are ignored, or at the very least, controlled, and personal and public spaces in schools are constructed in ways that limit physical contact between students as well as between students and teachers.

Of importance to note, I think, is the way that mind and body are split in attempts to reconcile the two within philosophical thought. A library search with the descriptor "mind-body" yields numerous sources that refer to the "mind-body problem" in philosophical thought. What is the "problem"? While reading about bodily knowing and spiritual knowing and ideas about re-enchanting the world (Moore and Berman), I did note some personal uneasiness at the outset of my readings. I did think I likely should not be reading about bodies and erotica and spiritual knowing and even magic. But there were so many enjoyable moments in that reading, and too many *"aha"* moments, to take these readings lightly.

In the wider Western world, outside the institution of education, acknowledging a spiritual knowing would go against the modern projects of progress and continued colonialism (in the form of multinational corporations). Recognizing a spiritual knowing of places would complicate the justification for plowing through a field to lay down an asphalt highway or airport runway. Modern-day subdivision growth might not be so prolific if we attended to and nurtured our spiritual knowings of places or if we believed we would be violating the spirit of the place to expand our urban landscapes. Ignoring the spirit of a place and spiritual knowing makes "progress" possible.

Travel Notes

Place: I am not sure

Linda Darling asked me to consider what Dewey might say about my research. "Maybe," she said, "he wouldn't go along with all of this."

I don't know what he would think about line dancing and poetic possibilities. I do think that he would be supportive of attempts to get over the perceived split between mind and body.

I can think back to my first master's seminar in curriculum theory, when Reg Flemming asked me if I would read *Democracy and Education* and then share my insights with the class. He called me "The Dewey Scholar" after that. Funny. Now I can hardly remember what I read about. But it is important to note how those who have theorized curriculum have in many ways cleared paths for people like me to travel down. The trouble is, I get caught in the ditches, wandering off, and before you know it I am way out in a field (but not always left field). Not really meaning to, but somehow I find myself wandering over to the shoulder of the road, and before you know it I am really in the ditch and in my panic I try to step on the brake and I hit the gas pedal instead, and then I am really off the beaten path.

Like right now I guess. Is this a musing? No. Okay. I will try to smarten up. Well, I think he might say,

> Collateral learning in the way of formation of enduring attitudes, of likes and dislikes, may be and often is much more important than the spelling lesson or lesson in geography or history that is learned. . . . What avail is it to win prescribed amounts of information about geography and history, to win ability to read and write, if in the process [we lose our] own soul: [lose our] appreciation of things worth while, of the values to which these things are relative . . . (*Experience and Education* 48–49)

Oops. He really *did* say that. Okay, I'll try again. What do *I* think he would say? Well, I do know that Dewey believed in the possibilities of an education that was based on ordinary experience, but he wanted to make sure there were some quality controls as to what counts as educational experience. He was criticized for his progressivism, or for the way it was taken up in schools without a lot of thought given to the kinds of experiences that were happening. I think this rampant progressivism in American schools is what Honeybone was referring to in his history of the school subject of geography (cited in Goodson). Honeybone was writing about how in the 1930s, geography became so generalized and covered so many areas that its purpose was lost, and he says this was partly due to the "spread 'under American influence' of a methodology, proclaiming that all education must be related to the everyday experience of the children" (64). And I do know that Dewey wasn't concerned with "isms" so much as he was concerned that education did not become a name or a slogan. In fact, he was sort of in a middle space, saying he didn't want total progressivism or total traditionalism.

Maybe he would say, "Well, I think embodied knowledge is a good thing, and we should find ways to encourage this within education, but we must not do something in the name of education just because we believe we are promoting embodied knowledge. There have to be reasons and some sort of quality control to all this. An activity or program that incorporates embodied knowledge must be educative in effect."

And then what would I say? Maybe I would say, "I agree that we should not find ways to incorporate embodied ways of knowing within curriculum just for the sake of acknowledging embodied knowledge. There should be educative reasons for wanting to include embodied knowledge in our teaching and learning."

Okay, here are some reasons:

- We should be including embodied knowledge in order to include multiple learning styles and to promote the most equitable educational practices possible.

- We should be including embodied knowledge in our learning experiences because abstract reasoning alone will not provide us with all there is to know about a concept or idea.

- We should be including embodied knowledge because embodied knowing is a dimension of human understanding that is present but often ignored; thus we often feel something is missing in our learning experiences.

In *Democracy and Education*, Dewey talked about the importance of not ignoring the body in education, but his reasons were rather functional. He noted how children become fidgety if they have to sit for long periods of time without actively engaging their bodies in a learning experience, and he said the result was "nervous strain and fatigue" on the part of the teacher and the student (141)!

What would Dewey say?

       We don't really know.

              Do we.

Place: Desk

When I talk about epistemology, I want to include a travel note about my day at the Vancouver Art Gallery, viewing the Matisse Jazz collection of cut-outs—the way his body dictated his art. He only began painting when he had appendicitis as a youth and was confined to bed; then, in his later life, bowel cancer and arthritis led him to sitting and the cut-outs. I could include this in some way as a cut-out, with collage, and use his techniques, and words, maps, bodies, print material in collage about bodies and minds.

Matisse thought that his line drawing was a direct translation of his emotion. I think he was privileging phenomenon and assuming a transparent line between his emotion and the lines he used to express that emotion. What if we considered how our line drawing affects our emotions, the two-way mingling, the line dancing between word and world, or between lines and living.

yellow creamy light from lamp
shadows from my hand and pen on the page
sometimes cause me to write in the shadows
and sometimes
because of the angle of my hand
I write outside the shadows
just on the edge of them

Desk Notes

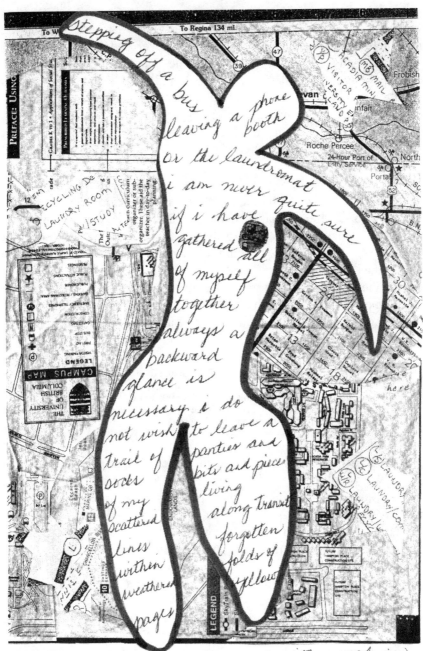

Stepping off a bus
leaving a phone booth
or the laundromat
i am never quite sure
if i have
gathered all
of myself
together
always a
backward
glance is
necessary i do
not wish to leave a
trail of panties and
socks bits and pieces
of my living
scattered along transit
lines forgotten
within folds of
weathered yellow
pages

with apologies...

So, then, how might we study the geographical notion of place in ways that attend to embodied knowing? And what about places we have never experienced? Places we have never been? Jeans calls for "an attention to literary skills and the imagination . . . in the education of the complete geographer" (13). The education Jeans is calling for requires a consideration of poetic language in our studies of place. Alongside our atlases and geography textbooks (perhaps even within them) we need to place poetry, and even novels and short stories. There are geo-graphy lessons to be learned from poets and storytellers.

The following geographical words taken from a Grade 8 geography textbook focus on interactions between humans and their environments, a theme that is studied regarding location and place in curricular geography: "Refer to the economic profiles of India and Burma on atlas p. 35A. Find the percentage that agriculture contributes to the Gross Domestic Product and the percentage of employment in agriculture . . ." (Kemball 83).

Human interaction with the environment is also evident in the following passage from Anita Rau Badami's best-selling novel, *Tamarind Mem*:

> The sweet odour of roses and rajni-gandha surrounding my father had seeped through the entire house. It was a dreadful smell, reminding me that Dadda was now just a body in the middle of the drawing room. He lay on a pile of rapidly melting ice, his mouth a thick blue line, cotton wool in his nostrils. . . . A warm draft puffed into the room . . . (143)

The above poetic words attend to bodies in spaces, to the ways in which the people who produce the Gross Domestic Product live and die. Because of cost factors, a high population, and space limitations in mortuaries, families in parts of India may arrange to have bodies of their loved ones in their homes while relatives pay their respects before cremation. Owing to climatic conditions, ice is often used to pack the bodies.

Poetic descriptions of places help us to connect our experiences of a place to the knowing of a place. One of the best parts about a weekend at Alice Lake in the Coast Mountain range of British Columbia, not far from Whistler Ski Resort, was a walk we took around the lake. Spending the morning lazily soaking up sun on the beach and in the water on air mattresses, we could see the people on the other side of the lake but we could not hear them. Luscious laziness lingered. As we walked along the path circling the lake, the shade from the trees provided a welcome coolness on our backs. I marveled at the thick green plant growth along the path through the trees, and I remember looking up to see how the sun could possibly make it through the trees to reach the undergrowth. The sunlight sparkled and filtered through the trees and landed on me in that very spot as I looked up. Some months later, I read the following lines from *Lake Ellenwood*, Leigh Faulkner's poem about a lake on the other side of the continent. As I read the words, I remembered and knew a place:

the campground is out of
sound
around the point;
at the far end of the lake
the corpulent lodge
lounges
on the beach;
the lambent sun catches in the treetops
and is passed down
from branch to branch . . . (31)

Moore refers to the depth and centrality of imagination that writing revives and speaks of a re-enchantment of the world, made possible through abandoning abstract philosophy and "mechanistic and mental approaches to the human situation":

> The life we make, for ourselves individually and for the world as a whole, is shaped and limited only by the perimeters of our imagination. Things are as we imagine them to be, as we imagine them into existence. Imagination is creativity, and the way we make our world depends on the vitality of our imagination. (380)

Perhaps there is a homeostatic relationship between imagination and landscape. The imagination we use to shape our world has also been shaped by our landscape. Hampl notes that "landscape plays a key role in the formation of the imagination . . . . It is the primer coat under all we can paint for ourselves and others" (125).

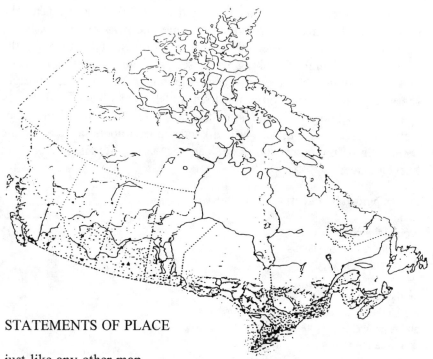

STATEMENTS OF PLACE

just like any other map
with dots punctuating places
small dots for small places
large dots for large places
on this map a large dot shows this place
Vancouver
like a period at the end of a statement

rolling down the map on prairie afternoons
we looked for places
we read the words beside the dots
not our dots
someone else lived in the dots we found
unlike the dot dwellers we lived in an unedited space
a dotless territory on the map
full of wind and gravel roads and sun
and in our sky jet streams left wispy lines
playing their game of connect the dots

"Place" is not a term that is used widely within current geographical curriculum materials. Location is the term used, and *finding* locations is the emphasis. While "local places" is the focus of study in the early grades, learning about our local places from Kindergarten to Grade 12 will not only enhance our notions of place and self, it will also present the possibility of creating a sense of responsibility and caring connections between land, people, and habitat. Sheila Harrington's *Giving the Land a Voice* was a project of local mapping that involved a bioregional approach to sustainable living on Salt Spring Island, off the west coast of Canada. Local people used drawings and writings to map their home places, with the results contributing to a social and cultural knowing of home places. Planners of the project state that "creating the maps was an attempt to reveal the essence of where we live, and how our community fits into a larger region. Until we have maps that do this, we risk being geographically located, but socially and culturally lost" (2).[37]

Several curricular scholars have argued for a curriculum that attends to lived experience and autobiographical knowledge. In attempts to answer the question of what is worth knowing, the self has been elevated to a place of importance. In his writings on autobiography and curriculum, Robert Graham[38] neatly positions autobiography within Dewey's ideas of constructing the self and relating to how the self is situated in society, the place of self-realization in education, and the social construction of knowledge. Dewey saw a progression from self-knowing to self-care. Embodied knowing and spiritual knowing of our everyday places would enhance what we know of ourselves, and would also present the possibility of exposing the realities of places and spaces. While the danger does exist in romanticizing place through poetics (though this is not always a dangerous project), validating personal, embodied knowings of place also presents possibilities for exploring the politics of place.

Human geography relegates importance to notions of space and place. Feminist geography recognizes the importance of local, lived everyday spaces, and how our spaces affect how we live our lives. What we know of our place and of locations is connected to what we know of ourselves and how we live in places and locations (our mingling dance of word/world). While place and self are seen as intimately connected, Doreen Massey looks at the cultural politics of space and place and addresses some of the ways in which the notion of place is problematic. She cautions that a "sense of place" can be constructed around "reactionary nationalisms," "competitive localisms," and "sanitized, introverted obsessions with 'heritage'" ("Power-Geometry" 64). Massey suggests that we begin to conceive of places as processes that are continuing to evolve and are not enclosed by boundaries; rather, they are defined by social relations and are composed of multiple identities, each of these qualities ensuring a continuing uniqueness of place. Geography as a discourse and as an active writing of the world supports this notion of place as a continuing, evolving process.

In her critique of the notion of place, Gillian Rose outlines that *place* is often equated with *home* in humanistic geography, and therefore relegated as feminine, nurturing, comforting, safe, and a place without conflict. While this might be the desired image of place/home constructed through patriarchal lenses, feminist geography acknowledges that place/home within this construction is often oppressive to women and marginalized people (*Feminism and Geography* 54–60). Humanistic geography took the position that to know a place was to be human, and this geographical perspective, which is not one and the same as "human" geography, was concerned with emotions and feelings and certain attachments to place. While Rose identifies humanistic (masculinist) constructions of place or home or community as feminine, she does acknowledge that humanistic geography pays attention to bodies in spaces, and embodied experiences of places, albeit masculine bodies.

In rather strong contrast to these critical examinations of place within academic human geography, Elspeth Deir has this to say about curricular geography: "Various skills specific to geography education emerge from concepts connected to space and place. These skills include the decoding of maps and globes, and the use and interpretation of symbols, direction, location, scales, and distance" (135). Her comment illustrates the way curricular geography skims the surface of notions of space and place, in a language of technology and indifference.

Embodied knowledge can be expressed in poetry about place; and while poetry can tell us that "the world is more wonderful than any of us have ever dared to guess" (Butala 56), it can also tell us that the

world is not wonderful. Poetic language can write the metonymic
spaces of a wonderful/not wonderful wor(l)de.

OH, CANADA

I went to your birthday party today
I saw your new helicopters and airplanes
and sea planes
I heard your military band play *Amazing Grace*
I tasted your Beaver Tails
dripping with Real Maple Syrup

        and O Canada
why were those men in red coats
showing us their dogs
and telling us how fast they could run
and how much fresh meat they could eat in just one day
and how fast the special highway cruiser car could go?

        and O Canada
who was that woman with the dark skin
wearing the blue coat
    cleaning up after all the dogs
    and the *Amazing Grace*
    and the people
        who dripped Real Maple Syrup
          onto the street
            when it melted
                under *all thy suns' command?*

LEARNING MY PLACE

I did not learn about my town
        how it came to be called Torquay
I did learn about Captain Vancouver and queen cities

I did not learn the population of my town
        no dot (between 0.1 and 0.5 million people)
        or square (more than 2 million people)
I did learn the three largest cities in Canada

I did not learn about the maps of my place
        how the numbers changed on them every three years
I did learn how others sold out and moved on when they could not live with the
numbers

I did not learn why only men went for three o'clock coffee
        at the Chinese Café on main street
I did learn that *As the World Turns* was always good on Fridays

I did not learn why my place
        was not as important as other places on the map
I did learn to live with invisibility

Place: Curricular Documents

While every curricular decision involves issues of ethics, I do need to say something about the ethical and moral dimensions of geography curriculum and poetic possibilities. My hope for geography curriculum is that we can make the study of geography more inclusive regarding method and content. One way of doing that is by attending to poetic language (a methodological/pedagogical and content consideration). Another way of doing that is to openly acknowledge how words can shape our worlds, and that worlds can shape our words, and that we can be actively involved in this process. In doing this we are creating a space for students to become aware of embodied knowledge and to become aware of the political nature of curriculum. There are many students who respond positively to activities that require an examination of text or creating text that is poetic.

Ethically and morally, if our curricular decisions leave out these kinds of experiences, we are creating a curriculum that excludes in its approaches to learning and to content. And we are prohibiting students from the fullest possible educational experiences. Perhaps poetry is more likely to be associated with feminine ways of expressing, and it could easily be assumed that we are being inequitable regarding gender and genre by excluding poetry; however, it is not just girls who are missing out when we devalue poetic textual practices. My own two boys are not that crazy about poetry, but it is true that a poem can say what it is very hard to express in other forms, and while they find poetry difficult to write, they do like to read poems (even mine) and "figure them out." They always have insights that are instructive to me.

The Goodlad, Soder, and Sirotnik collection of articles about the moral dimensions of teaching is worth looking at here. In this collection, Walter Feinberg notes that the "role of public education is to create and recreate a public by giving voice to an otherwise inarticulate, uninformed mass" (181). I don't agree with the last part of his statement, and maybe he doesn't either, because he does go on to say that "the idea of a public suggests, as Dewey well understood, a sense of shared experience and symbols for communicating the meaning of that experience to others" (182). And he does say that creating and re-creating a public requires attending to everyday knowledge. (So he can't be thinking that this everyday knowledge is coming from an "uninformed, inarticulate mass.") Anyway, concerning the moral dimensions of teaching, Feinberg notes the importance of considering individual development and *emotional and intellectual* growth of students when teachers make professional judgments about curriculum.

Another article in this collection, by Kenneth Sirotnik ("Society, Schooling, Teaching, and Preparing to Teach"), talks about an ethics of inquiry, knowledge, competence, caring, and social justice. He indicates that, where ethics are concerned, social justice is a bottom line regarding public education. He sees signs of social injustice in our schools: tracking students, selective curriculum for selective students, "unidimensional tests of intelligence" (312).

Not questioning what it is we do in geography lessons, and why we do it, is an example of social injustice. One of the main reasons that geography is included in social studies education is to promote nationalism and civic competence (but this is not often stated in curricular rationale statements). This point should be noted in teacher education courses, and teachers themselves should be making this point evident to students.

When we study locations in classrooms, we should ask students to note what we study and what we do not study. And we should encourage students to question. For example, why does the Canadian national anthem refer to "all thy sons"? Is that an inclusive phrase? Does language matter? What about the notion of Saskatchewan as the "prairie province" or the "plains"? If we travel above 54° latitude in Saskatchewan we find out that "prairie" is full of lakes and trees and outcroppings of solid rock. And the people who live there do not believe they live on a prairie. Maybe they start to believe that they are invisible. Social justice requires critical reflection regarding method and content on the part of teachers, and it requires encouraging students to critically reflect on these issues as well.

Maybe the bottom line is to ask some questions, such as: What is unethical about including poetry in our study of geography? What is unethical about validating embodied knowledge in our approach to geography, in how we come to understand issues and ourselves? What is unethical about questioning the history of maps or the language of scientific, objective approaches to learning about spaces and places? I cannot, at this point, think of any good answers to these questions.

Which places are ordinarily studied in North American classrooms and why and how? Envision this: A double-page spread in the *National Geographic* publication *Geography for Life*.[39] The page is black and shows the world from space, lit up at night. The photo explanation points to gas burn-off areas in the Persian Gulf region: "Imagine what this would have looked like during the Gulf War in 1991," and an area in the Sea of Japan where "there is a valuable resource being exploited. . . . It is the Japanese squid-fishing fleet, lit up at night for round-the-clock harvesting." *I thought that war was over . . .* The photo title is "The World at Night," and the explanation accompanying the photo begins with:

> Light is evidence of large numbers of people and cities; dark means the absence of people and cities. You can see great clusters of cities—from Boston through New York, Philadelphia, and Baltimore, to Washington. This is the original megalopolis, the nation's economic and political powerhouse. (12)

What if I live in the dark, in the absence of people and cities? Or what if I live in an economic and political powerhouse, but come to school hungry, or sick from the fumes of the industrial park that pumps up and fuels the economic and political powerhouse? In many cases, it seems that the places we study in classrooms are the "bright lights" places, or other places in the world that affect how we maintain our economic and political powerhouses.

Several writers illustrate how poetry can be political. Postcolonial writing examines the way the world is written and seeks to rewrite or poem the world in more inclusive ways. Jamaica Kincaid writes about her place and how it was not the place the English wanted it to be, and so during the colonial period, Antigua was turned into England, "but no place could really ever be England, and nobody who did not look exactly like them could ever be English, so you can imagine the destruction of people and land that came from that" (92).

As Veronica Strong-Boag notes, Pauline Johnson was intent on remapping the Canadian "imaginative landscape" with her poetry and words. Regarding the geography of Vancouver and the Pacific coast, Johnson reminds readers that the "twin peaks which rose to the north of the city are not 'the lions' appropriated by some foreign-born settler. . . . The mountains had a far older indigenous history as the 'sisters' of Indian legend" (55–56).

Along with the political significance of the places we study, there are ethical and moral issues at stake. When curriculum ignores our everyday lived spaces, it in effect erases people and places from the map, as well as issues and problems. Current events bulletin boards in classrooms that feature a map with pins stuck into newsworthy places around the world ignore local, everyday places and experiences. Students recognize that a famine on the other side of the world is horrendous, while they step around homeless people just around the corner from the bus stop. And children learn to believe that their place is not so important—unless it happens to be one of the large dots on political maps of the territory, and even so, it is studied in disembodied ways, with lived experience ignored, especially those experiences of the unempowered.

Poetic possibilities for writing the world in personal, embodied ways are present within poststructural approaches to reading/writing and within poetic language.

And yes
I do believe
geography classrooms are places
where handling the moonlight is possible.

THE SUPPLEMENT[40]
10 WAYS TO HANDLE MOONLIGHT

I

Moon shadows surround the sleeping children.
In the morning they will wake and return to desks that hold their
secret treasures:
    sample tubes of AVON lipstick rocks and sticks that are just that
    size bits of chalk the janitor missed in sweeping torn pieces of
    tissue paper
In the morning they will wonder:
    where does the rain come from why is the toilet paper so scratchy
    in the school washrooms what is in the teacher's desk where is that
    smell coming from
In the moonlight they murmur and dream. Some dream to remember
some dream to forget.

II

in the moonlight
       your hands
              my dress
                  the wet grass
                      the way a breeze played with your hair
                            it was my 30th birthday

III

at three I rise
and go down to the lake
I paddle down past the golf course,
open a bottle of wine
and let the wind

take me back

it is here,
by moonlight,
that I have come . . .

. . . there are things greater than trout,
shadows in the deeper pools,
passing beneath
the keel of my canoe[41]

IV

For a very long time I have felt myself to be in a poetic and
fantasmatic relationship to the moon our other . . . to whom I always
say—silently looking at her—excuse me for acting as if you were the
other, whereas you are *lune*. Let us change points of view . . . . in this
case the other would be the earth. And it is a good thing. Each one
should get her or his turn . . . . the earth seen from the point of view
of the moon is revived: It is unknown, to be rediscovered.[42]

V

In the morning they will write their world with numbers and lines and
colours and words. Their words will speak of their places and their
words will not always rhyme. In the moonlight they murmur and
dream.

VI

*I have a personal belief that when women of all nations/colours pass
from this world to the spirit world part of their spirit goes into the
moon.*[43]
    Who will I have when you leave me here? I am afraid.
    *You will have your Moon to keep you company, inside and above
you.*[44]

VII

And sometimes, by the light of the moon, they cross the line. They write on top of lines already written. They draw in their own lines. They fold up their maps and make them fly. They open their atlases and begin to read/write their stories between the lines. And they map the spaces in their world that only they can map, as they move and breathe and dance through spaces. They hear the stories of other times and places they have not traveled through, and they understand their living in their own places just a little more. And they know a little more about the intimate spaces within.

VIII

what to do with all her shoes
we sat by a dusty closet wondering
if the red ones would still fit
and what about underwear
and for some reason
the men that came
to my mother's house
after my grandmother's burial
took their shoes off at the door
maybe custom or caution
or superstition
not to scatter dust
from the grounds of the remains
on the grounds of the remaining
her brother Lawrence from the second floor
and down across
wanted to leave
but his shoes were not at the door
someone else
had worn them home
and left him with a smaller smoother newer pair
in stocking feet
remembering dampness
and the wild playfulness of august evenings

Uncle Lawrence left
in the moonlight
later in the fall
shoes exchanged
through the mail
and maybe a letter
saying sorry I took your shoes
they were a little big
and a returned note saying
thanks for sending my shoes
yours were just too small

IX

Here there are only shadows. The moonlight is a memory now and left behind are lines of wind and darkness. The children have grown up and they move out into the world—the one they have written. The one they continue to write. Every now and then they add a comma, delete a sentence, write a new pali-graph[45] to their palimpsest prairie criss-crossings and overlays of moonlight trails. Some things only happen in the moonlight and these things we do not always notice. But the traces are there. We hear and see and smell and dream the traces moving over and within us.

X

moonlight
    as aphrodisiac 88–99; grass is always wet
    in the 77–78; how to catch the 91–94;
    lake surfaces and 3, 8, 39–41, 111–114;
    leaving the tent without a flashlight and noting
    the 101–105; needing extra money and
    deciding to 28, 46–51, 60n, 87; parking and 55, 59n;
    places to walk in the 19–21, 33n; and the places
    where words stop 45–79; see also 'poetry',
    'embodied knowledge(s)', 'line dancing'

GENERAL INDEX

DANCING INSTRUCTIONS

there is space

imagine
    stepping into the space

imagine
    the intricate changes
    your body brings
    to the space
    on the dance floor
    just by being

        even a toe

            skimming surface

                    creates a line

            of exquisite space

NOTES

1. I am referring here and throughout this atlas to school geography in the North American context. School geography in North America lags behind academic geography (a distinction I discuss further on) in its incorporation of critical reflection and theoretical and analytical thinking. However, when it comes to academic geography, the North American context is similar to the rest of the Western world regarding the current attention to issues of poetics, politics, social theory, and critical reflection regarding what geography is/does.

2. I use the terms *embody, embodied, embodiment* to refer to human lived experience, and also to refer to our physical bodies, body parts, and bodily experiences.

3. Even while I write lines, I see spaces. Lines call space into presence. The presence of lines indicates the presence of space in the same instant. Could there be a line without a space? Could we recognize a space without the presence of a line? I use the term *space* to refer to space on a page of paper, school spaces, curricular spaces, imagined spaces, and metaphorical and metonymical spaces. Lines from bell hooks on space: "Spaces can be real and imagined. Spaces can tell stories and unfold histories. Spaces can be interrupted, appropriated, and transformed through artistic and literary practice" (*Yearning* 152).

4. "Few other places of work exemplify patriarchal rule better than the university, from the bureaucratic distribution of power to the Foucauldian 'network of writing' (1979) rationalized in the rule system of the form and memo that administer procedure, persons, and knowledge" (Carmen Luke and Jennifer Gore 202).

A Guide to the Atlas

5. See Alison Lee, 1996, and Frances Slater, 1989. These studies inquire into the role of language in learning. They take the position that experience is mediated by language, and that language is a cultural artifact arising out of dominant ideologies. These scholars imply that we need to become critical of the language used in the teaching of geography in order to interrupt the power of the dominant language, and that the dominant scientific discourse in geography teaching and learning excludes students according to race, gender, and class.

    One of the premises of this atlas is that while language is indeed an ideological construct representing dominant cultural ideologies, it is necessary to view language and experience as *both* involved in signification. It is the poetics of signifying that I inquire into, in order to build support for transforming our world writing. Human agency is possible through a deliberate choice of genres in our study of geography—we can consciously enter into the line dance of signification. What Lee and Slater touch on only briefly is that our study of geography, of world-writing, *is* our world writing.

Chapter One: Line Dancing

6. All of this talk of signifiers and signifieds relates back to Saussure and his theories of semiotics; however, many additions to his science of the sign have occurred. Saussure was concerned only with the sign, and not with what has since been added to equations—the referent and the subject. My use of signifier and signified actually refers to components of more recent semiotic theory; where "signifier" signifies word and "signified" signifies world (referent). Regarding relationships, Saussure was concerned only with the relationship between the signifier and the signified (the phonic and mental components), between a sign and all other signs in a signifying event, and between signs in a closed system. While

he spoke of the sign as having two parts—signifier (in this case an actual phonetic component) and signified (in this case a mental image called forth by the signifier), he did not consider what might be outside of the sign, a component later referred to as the "referent" by Peirce. While semiotics began as a science of the sign, its work has evolved to include not only the sign, but the referent (object) and the subject as well. So although Saussure saw language as very important in considering social phenomena, he did not consider anything outside of the sign and other signs in his study of the sign. A strange contradiction, considering that he first began to think of a "science which studies the role of signs as part of social life" (15). He was separating out signs from us(e).

7. Ted Aoki, 1996. Ted encourages curriculum scholars to consider the space between a signification that privileges *world* as Discourse A; and a signification that privileges *spaces between words* (i.e., the space of difference between words) as Discourse B. He proposes a discourse or model for signification that is Discourse A and/not and Discourse B: a Metonymical Discourse C.

8. I like Terry Threadgold's definition of theory. She speaks of theory as stories told from some body's position (1). When I speak of theory, I am speaking of ideas or thoughts about something (rather than facts or practices). Five speculative, fanciful theories on writing and living after 40:

    1. Never fabricate a citation unless it suits your purposes.
    2. Keep a list of interesting names from your favorite novels. These are very useful for fabricating citations.
    3. We cannot all be Julia Kristeva or Hélène Cixous. Honor their words and believe in yourself.
    4. If you have a feeling about something, trust that feeling.
    5. If you want to feel young, go to matinée theatre performances where the AAA (Average Age in Attendance) $\geq$ 75. And have your hair styled only by

people much older than you (they will know you are younger, and will style your hair accordingly).

9.   Ted Aoki, letter to the author, 19 June 1998. Ted notes that this imaginary Discourse B can be described as "In the beginning is the word "word" (Sr) and the word "world" (Sr)." "Word" and "world" is an intertextual relationship of signifiers within a floating discursive space.

10.   Is this small piece of language, one word, yet many, what Metaphor with a capital M presents/performs? Is everything? Similarity in a system depends on contiguity (and also on difference).

Post-note: After speaking with Ted Aoki, and reading again my references that deal with metonymic writing and metaphoric writing, this is what I understand: Metaphoric discourse is a discourse of verticality, an effort to mime what is not present and in the mimetic act, to call the absence to presence. There is a privileging of presence within this discourse, and it is similar to Ted's imaginary Discourse A. Discourse B is a discourse that plays with the difference between word and word, capitalizing on that difference between Sr and Sr, and privileging absence, and this is metonymic discourse, with a small m. Metonymic discourse with a capital M (Metonymy) is that "and/not and" of metaphor/metonymy, and this is Ted's imaginary Discourse C. And here is where my notion of worlde resides, and where poetic possibilities for new dancing steps exist.

Chapter Two: Landscapes of Geography

11.   It is interesting to note that the discussions of Pinar and his colleagues regarding curricular matters are filled with cartographical metaphors; in fact, the index includes 19 direct references to mapping—in a book dealing with curriculum! Phrases such as "mapped fields," "mapping theories of curriculum," "plotting a journey," "the curricular outline as

map," "mapping dominant positions in curricular theory" are located frequently throughout the text. A discussion of jan jagodzinski's work (490) is filled with mapping metaphors and is concerned with a "dismantling of male dominance and technical rationality" (all the while using a system of metaphors that has typically been associated with male dominance and technical precision). However, in a related book chapter, jan jagodzinski does discuss spaces for possibility regarding maps and curriculum. jagodzinski describes curricular documents as maps that we might use for traveling, and he notes that it is when the travel route becomes predetermined through the territory/map/curriculum that these maps/curricular documents lose their openness to possibility (*Curriculum as Felt through Six Layers* 162).

12. See Shields, 1994, for a discussion of Benjamin's writing on the *flâneur*.

13. While North American curriculum had its origins in British and French curricular traditions, it is unlikely that present-day geography curriculum in North America parallels Britain's. However, Goodson's study is useful because it highlights the territorial boundary between the academy and the schoolyard, and the possibilities that open up when this boundary is transgressed.

14. Here I am referring to those educators who study curriculum and consider policy and programming and changes to curricular planned lines, and who (like myself) have the opportunity to work within the curricular lines and spaces of teacher education programs. Classroom teachers may be attending quite closely to recent developments in academic geography on an individual basis, but any related innovations have not translated into curricular documents (curriculum-as-planned). There are certainly teachers who throw out the curriculum documents and go their own way. My concern is with a transformation in the curriculum-as-planned. In our conversations regarding curriculum-as-planned we need to become more attuned to recent developments in academic

geography in order to create more possibilities for transformation of curricula-as-live(d).

15. British Columbia, *Grade 6 Instructional Resource Package*, 62. Italics added.

16. British Columbia, *Grade 1 Instructional Resource Package*, 20. Italics added.

17. Joseph Kirman, *Elementary Social Studies* (99). Italics added.

18. When I speak of social studies education, I am referring to the area of study as it is constructed within teacher education documents, curricular documents, and in curricular discussions within scholarly writing and research. I am not speaking here of "doing" the subject of social studies; but rather how it is constructed as a subject area.

19. British Columbia, *1996 BC Assessment of Social Studies: Highlights*, 8–9.

20. Lyn Hejinian notes that:

> description should not be confused with definition; it is not definitive but transformative. Description . . . is a particular and complicated process of thinking, highly intentional while at the same time ideally simultaneous with and equivalent to perception (and thus open to the arbitrariness, unpredictability, and inadvertence of what appears). (32)

21. Lynn Hejinian notes the similarity between the records made by explorers and records of dreams. She notes there is "the same apparent objectivity, the same attempt to be accurate about details and to be equally accurate about every detail (presumably because one doesn't know which details are important ones, either in Tahiti or in the dream)" (33).

22. The government documents were for the most part provincial documents from two Canadian provinces where I have been involved in social studies education. Further on in this atlas, consideration is given to the National Standards for

Geography that have been adopted within the United States (these same standards are receiving some attention within the Canadian curricular context, but the full extent of the attention is not known).

23. Because this curricular exploration is concerned with the dance between living and planning, I chose to explore documents that have been a part of my own curricular dancing for several years. Government curriculum documents from the provinces of British Columbia and Saskatchewan regarding geography teaching and learning were therefore examined. Understandings that are labeled geographical are located within the curriculum organizer (unit of study) "Environment" in the British Columbia ministry documents and geographical emphasis was noted within the unit of study "Identity" in Saskatchewan education documents.

24. Thank you to Derek Gregory for his guidance with this general overview.

25. Hillis focuses on this relationship as one with history, and how the disembodied perspective had implications for "Discovery."

26. Of course, even as I wandered about exploring the various curricular documents, I was aware that I was also involved in "constructing" or "describing" geography. I was looking for certain attributes, certain phrases, that would lend clues to the structures and constructions already in place (like my noting of the concepts that are considered to be geographical). I was looking for certain artifacts, certain souvenirs, if you will, to take back home with me, to show the reader (including myself as a reader). I consider geography a subject discipline that holds possibilities for continuous construction, a place where spaces continue to open up to possibilities.

27. While you might be thinking here, "As long as we write poetry or creative lines about spaces and places in some

subject, what does it matter if it is not in 'geography' class?"
The thing is, separating out genres and leaving scientific
language to the study of geography continues to perpetuate a
detached writing of the world. And saving poetic language for
other school subjects usually means saving poetic language
for topics not related to space and place. It is an important
issue to consider—we need that added dimension within our
world writing in order to connect more personally with
ourselves/others and worlds.

28. As I indicated earlier, school geography in North America
     lags behind academic geography regarding critical reflection
     and linking geographical matters with contemporary social
     theory. *New Zealand Journal of Geography* contains a nice
     mix of theoretical articles and practical articles. It mixes
     genres and audience appeal as well. Both academics and
     practitioners will find stimulating reading in this journal, and
     the journal provides the space for academics and practitioners
     to keep in touch through sharing their research and literature.

29. There are several obvious parallels between social studies
     education and feminist geography perspectives. A basic tenet
     of feminist geography—questioning and critiquing the
     construction of geography—supports the goals of
     participatory citizenship and questioning and challenging
     through critical thinking, advocated within social studies
     education. Further parallels can be seen in the recent trend
     within social studies education that requires students to
     become involved in field studies in their local communities,
     and in the feminist geographical acknowledgment of local,
     situated research. While social studies has traditionally been
     concerned largely with the public sphere, Nel Noddings is a
     scholar who promotes feminist perspectives within social
     studies education. She points out that while any sharp
     "separation between [public and private] breaks down under
     analysis, the tradition that sustains the separation is still
     dominant. Surely if we had started with private life, the school
     curriculum would be very different from the one actually
     developed" (234). Like Noddings, feminist geographers

support the inclusion of the private sphere in research and writing, and attempt to envision a more fluid boundary between the two (that is, private spaces often merge on public spaces and vice versa).

30.　See Alison Lee, 1996. This study examines the gendered nature of the content and language practices of geography in Australian high school classrooms and the barriers this gender bias presents for females to succeed. Lee also critiques previous studies of the language of school science that were based on linguistic analysis as being inadequate because of the technical and scientific nature of the language of linguistic studies itself, which presents barriers to a critical analysis.

CHAPTER THREE: POETIC POSSIBILITIES

31.　I like Roland Barthes's notion of text in *The Semiotic Challenge*:

> It is not an esthetic product, it is a signifying practice; it is not a structure, it is a structuration; it is not an object, it is a work and a game [like a dance . . .]; it is not a group of closed signs, endowed with a meaning to be rediscovered, it is a volume of traces in displacement. (7)

32.　See Carol Martin, ed. *Local Colour*, 1994; Constance Rook, ed. *Writing Home*, 1997; and Terry Glavin, *This Ragged Place: Travels Across the Landscape*, 1996.

33.　Monmonier, 1996. Monmonier classifies way-finding maps as folk cartography.

34.　Michel Foucault discusses the panoptical view in *Discipline and Punish*. It is a view from a tower, like those in the prison yards. People in the tower have an "all seeing" eye. They can survey from on high and get the whole picture in one totalizing gaze. While some might not agree that maps and our traditional use of maps exemplify the panopticon (it might not appear that behavior is altered because of the panoptical view/presence within the tradition of mapping), I do believe that our traditional use and reading of maps does alter our behavior. We adopt a detached, disembodied position in relation to the world presented in maps.

35.   "definition." *Gage Canadian Dictionary*, 410.

36.   And this relates to my earlier note regarding the proliferation of "map skills" in geography curriculum and the panoptical effects of this detached study.

37.   While the planners were subscribing to a representational discourse, hoping their project would reveal the "essence" of their community and the larger region, their mapping project was also a writing of their community and the larger region, a performance in the space between a representational (revealing) discourse and a floating (concealing) discourse.

38.   See Robert Graham, 1991.

39.   *National Geography Standards 1994*; p. 12. While "place" is considered, the focus through much of this publication is on economic power and global competition: "standards reflect the belief that geography must be as rigorously taught in the United States as it is in other countries. All countries depend upon their citizens' knowledge of the world to compete in the global economy . . ." (237). Also, owing to a critical examination of photojournalism in *National Geographic* (see Lutz and Collins, 1993), my reading of *National Geographic* has become one of skepticism and critique. I noted this same "geography for life (read global competition)" aspect within the teacher education textbook *Geography for Educators*, which is based on *National Geography Standards 1994*. This text lists "geographic illiteracy" as something to be "combatted":

> We depend on a well-informed populace to maintain the democratic ideals which have made this country great. When 95 percent of some of our brightest college students cannot locate Vietnam on a world map, we must sound the alarm. In 1980, a presidential commission found that companies in the United States fare poorly against foreign competitors, in part because Americans are

ignorant of things beyond their borders." (Hardwick and
Holtgrieve 2)

THE SUPPLEMENT

40.   In my old school atlas there were two sections: the atlas and
      the supplement. I have used that format for this atlas. I like the
      notion of supplement as coming after, added on; it can only
      be a supplement because of what came before; it calls forth
      that which it is not. Checking with a dictionary, I noted a
      reference to supplement: "to supplement one's income"
      (*Gage Canadian Dictionary*, 1470). Isn't that moonlighting?

41.   Leigh Faulkner, 1993 (32).

42.   Hélène Cixous, 1997 (10).

43.   Cat Cayuga, quoted in Lenore Keeshig-Tobias, 1996, no
      pagination. Italics added.

44.   Barbara LaValley, quoted in Lenore Keeshig-Tobias, 1996, no
      pagination. Italics added.

45.   Erika Hasebe-Ludt describes a palagraphic text as one that
      "reflects its layered textuality in the form of different types of
      fonts and spatial arrangements for the shifting voices" of
      many (210).

REFERENCES

Abram, David. *The Spell of the Sensuous (Perception and Language in a More-than-Human World)*. New York: Vintage Books, 1997.

Ackerman, Diane. *A Natural History of the Senses*. New York: Vintage Books, 1991.

Aoki, Ted. "In the Midst of Language Education and Global Education." *Thinking Globally About Language Education*. Eds. Marilyn Chapman and James Anderson. Vancouver, BC: Research and Development in Global Studies, 1995. 191–198.

_____. *Modernity and Postmodernity: Implications for Education*. Paper presented at KEDI; May, 1996.

_____. Letter to author, 19 June 1998.

Bachelard, Gaston. *The Poetics of Space*. Trans. Maria Jolas. Boston: Beacon Press, 1964. Trans. of *La Poétique de l'espace*. 1958.

Badami, Anita Rau. *Tamarind Mem*. Toronto, ON: Penguin, 1996.

Barnes, Trevor, and James Duncan, eds. *Writing Worlds: Discourse, Metaphor and Text in the Representation of Landscape*. New York: Routledge, 1992.

Barthes, Roland. *S/Z*. Trans. Richard Miller. New York: Hill and Wang, 1974. Trans. of *S/Z*. 1970.

_____. *The Rustle of Language*. Trans. Richard Howard. Berkeley: University of California Press, 1986. Trans. of *Le bruissement de la langue*. 1984.

_____. *The Semiotic Challenge*. Trans. Richard Howard. Berkeley: University of California Press, 1988. Trans. of *L'aventure semiologique*. 1985.

Bartz Petchenik, Barbara. "The Natural History of the Atlas/Evolution and Extinction." *Cartographica* 22.3 (1985): 43–59.

Benko, Georges, and Ulf Strohmayer, eds. *Space and Social Theory: Interpreting Modernity and Postmodernity*. Oxford, UK: Blackwell, 1997.

Berman, Morris. *The Reenchantment of the World*. Ithaca, NY: Cornell University Press, 1981.

Bondi, Liz. "Other Figures in Other Places: On Feminism, Postmodernism and Geography." *Environment and Planning D: Society and Space* 10 (1992): 199–213.

British Columbia. Ministry of Education, Skills and Training. *1996 BC Assessment of Social Studies: Highlights*. Victoria, BC, 1997.

British Columbia. Ministry of Education, Skills and Training. *Geography 12 Integrated Resource Package 1997*. Victoria, BC, 1997.

British Columbia. Ministry of Education, Skills and Training. *Social Studies K to 7 Integrated Resource Package 1996*. Victoria, BC, 1996.

Butala, Sharon. *The Perfection of the Morning: An Apprenticeship in Nature*. Toronto, ON: HarperCollins, 1994.

de Certeau, Michel. *The Practice of Everyday Life*. Trans. Steven Rendall. Berkeley: University of California Press, 1984. Trans. of *Arts de faire*. 1974.

Chapin, June, and Rosemary Messick. *Elementary Social Studies: A Practical Guide*. New York: Longman, 1999.

Choy, Wayson. "The Ten Thousand Things." *Writing Home.* Ed. Constance Rooke. Toronto, ON: McClelland & Stewart, 1997. 13–22.

Cixous, Hélène, and Mireille Calle-Gruber. *Rootprints: Memory and Life Writing.* Trans. Eric Prenowitz. New York: Routledge, 1997. Trans. of *Photos de Racine.* 1994.

Clifford, James. *Routes: Travel and Translation in the Late Twentieth Century.* Cambridge: Harvard University Press, 1997.

Collins, Jeff, and Bill Mayblin. *Derrida for Beginners.* Cambridge, UK: Icon Books, 1996.

Connelly, Karen. *Touch the Dragon: A Thai Journal.* Winnipeg, MN: Turnstone Press, 1992.

Cosgrove, Denis. "Prospect, Perspective and the Evolution of the Landscape Idea." *Transactions, Institute of British Geographers* 10 (1985): 45–62.

Deir, Elspeth. "The Place of Geography within Social Studies." *Trends and Issues in Canadian Social Studies.* Eds. Ian Wright and Alan Sears. Vancouver, BC: Pacific Educational Press, 1997. 130–146.

Deleuze, Gilles, and Felix Guattari. *On the Line.* Trans. John Johnston. New York: Columbia University Press, 1983.

Demorest, Margaret. "Thirteen Ways of Looking at a Poem: Poetry as Play." *Counterbalance: Gendered Perspectives for Writing and Language.* Ed. Carolyn Logan. Peterborough, ON: Broadview Press, 1997. 359–372.

Derrida, Jacques. *Dissemination.* Trans. Barbara Johnson. Chicago: University of Chicago Press, 1981. Trans. of *La Dissémination.* 1972.

Dewey, John. *Democracy and Education*. New York: The Free Press, 1916.

_____. *Experience and Education*. New York: Collier, 1938.

Driver, Felix. "New Perspectives on the History and Philosophy of Geography." *Progress in Human Geography* 18.1 (1994): 92–100.

Eisner, Elliot. *Cognition and Curriculum Reconsidered*. New York: Teachers College Press, 1994.

_____. "The Promise and Perils of Alternative Forms of Data Representation." *Educational Researcher* 26.6 (1997): 4–10.

Faulkner, Leigh. *Where the Fields End: Poems Selected and New*. Alma, NB: Owl's Head Press, 1993.

Feinberg, Walter. "The Moral Responsibility of Public Schools." *The Moral Dimensions of Teaching*. Eds. John Goodlad, Roger Soder and Kenneth Sirotnik. San Francisco: Jossey-Bass Publications, 1990. 155–170.

Foucault, Michel. *Discipline and Punish: The Birth of the Prison*. Trans. Alan Sheridan. New York: Vintage Books, 1977. Trans. of *Surveiller et Punir: Naissance de la Prison*. 1975.

Geography Education Standards Project. *Geography for Life*. Washington, DC: National Geographic Research & Exploration, 1994.

Glavin, Terry. *This Ragged Place: Travels Across the Landscape*. Vancouver, BC: New Star Books, 1996.

Goodlad, John, Roger Soder, and Kenneth Sirotnik, eds. *The Moral Dimensions of Teaching*. San Francisco: Jossey-Bass Publications, 1990.

Goodson, Ivor. *School Subjects and Curriculum Change: Studies in Curriculum History*. Washington, DC: The Falmer Press, 1993.

Gordimer, Nadine. *Writing and Being*. Cambridge: Harvard University Press, 1995.

Graham, Robert. *Reading and Writing the Self: Autobiography in Education and Curriculum*. New York: Teachers College Press, 1991.

Gregory, Derek. *Geographical Imaginations*. Cambridge: Blackwell, 1994.

Haggett, Peter. *The Geographer's Art*. Cambridge: Blackwell, 1990.

Hampl, P. "In the Mountain Ranges and Forests of St. Paul." *Imagining Home: Writing from the Midwest*. Eds. M. Vinz and T. Tammaro. Minneapolis: University of Minnesota Press, 1995. 123–128.

Hardwick, Susan, and Donald Holtgrieve. *Geography for Educators: Standards, Themes, and Concepts*. Upper Saddle River, NJ: Prentice-Hall, 1996.

Harley, J. B. "Deconstructing the Map." *Writing Worlds: Discourse, Text and Metaphor in the Representation of Landscape*. Eds. Trevor Barnes and James Duncan. New York: Routledge, 1992. 231–247.

Harrington, Sheila, ed. *Giving the Land a Voice: Mapping Our Home Places*. Salt Spring Island, BC: Salt Spring Island Community Services Society, 1994.

Hasebe-Ludt, Erika. "In All the Universe: Placing the Texts of Culture and Community in Only One School." Ph.D. Diss. University of British Columbia, 1995.

Heidegger, Martin. *Poetry, Language, Thought*. Trans. Albert Hofstadter. New York: Harper & Row, 1971.

Hejinian, Lyn. "Strangeness." *Poetics* 8 (1989): 32–45.

Henley, Richard. "The Ideology of Geographical Language." *Language and Learning in the Teaching of Geography*. Ed. Frances Slater. New York: Routledge, 1989. 162–171.

Heshusius, Lous, and Keith Ballard, eds. *From Positivism to Interpretivism and Beyond: Tales of Transformation in Educational and Social Research (The Mind-Body Connection)*. New York: Teachers College Press, 1996.

Hillis, Ken. "The Power of Disembodied Imagination: Perspective's Role in Cartography." *Cartographica* 31.3 (1994): 1–17.

hooks, bell. *Yearning: Race, Gender, and Cultural Politics*. Toronto, ON: Between the Lines, 1990.

_____. "Representing Whiteness in the Black Imagination." *Cultural Studies*. Eds. Lawrence Grossberg, Cary Nelson, and Paula Treichler. New York: Routledge, 1992. 338–346.

Hospital, Janette Turner. *Isobars*. Baton Rouge: Louisiana State University Press, 1990.

Humphreys, Helen. *The Perils of Geography*. London, ON: Brick Books, 1995.

jagodzinski, jan. "Curriculum as Felt through Six Layers of an Aesthetically Embodied Skin: The Arch-Writing on the Body." *Understanding Curriculum as Phenomenological and Deconstructed Text*. Eds. William Pinar and William Reynolds. New York: Teachers College Press, 1992. 159–183.

Jardine, David. *To Dwell with a Boundless Heart: Essays in Curriculum Theory, Hermeneutics, and the Ecological Imagination*. New York: Peter Lang, 1998.

Jeans, D. "Some Literary Examples of Humanistic Descriptions of Place." *Australian Geographer* 14.4 (1979): 207–214.

Keeshig-Tobias, Lenore, ed. *Into the Moon: Heart, Mind, Body, Soul.* Toronto, ON: Sister Vision, 1996.

Kemball, W. *Geographic Essentials: Map Skills Using the Canadian Oxford School Atlas 5th Edition B.C.* Toronto, ON: Oxford University Press, 1986.

Kim, Kyong. *Caged in Our Signs: A Book about Semiotics.* Norwood, NJ: Ablex, 1996.

Kincaid, Jamaica. "A Small Place." *The Post-Colonial Studies Reader.* Eds. Bill Ashcroft, Gareth Griffiths, and Helen Tiffin. New York: Routledge, 1995. 92–94.

Kirby, Kathleen. "Re:Mapping Subjectivity: Cartographic Vision and the Limits of Politics." *Body Space.* Ed. Nancy Duncan. New York: Routledge, 1996. 45–55.

Kirman, Joseph. *Elementary Social Studies* (2nd Ed.). Scarborough, ON: Allyn & Bacon Canada, 1996.

Kristeva, Julia. "Revolution in Poetic Language." *The Portable Kristeva.* Ed. Kelly Oliver. New York: Columbia University Press, 1997.

Lather, Patti. "Post-Critical Pedagogies: A Feminist Reading." *Feminisms and Critical Pedagogy.* Eds. Carmen Luke and Jennifer Gore. New York: Routledge, 1992. 120–137.

Lauterbach, Ann. *And for Example.* New York: Penguin, 1994.

Lee, Alison. *Gender, Literacy, Curriculum: Re-Writing School Geography.* Brisbane, Australia: Taylor & Francis, 1996.

Leggo, Carl. "Living Ungrammatically in a Grammatical World: The Pedagogic World of Teachers and Students." *Interchange* 29.2 (1998): 169–184.

_____. "Grade Four Geography." *View from My Mother's House.* St. John's, NF: Killick Press, 1999. 39

Longhurst, Robyn, and Robin Peace. "Lecture Theatre to Classroom—Feminist Geography." *New Zealand Journal of Geography* 96 (1993): 16–18.

Luke, Carmen, and Jennifer Gore. "Women in the Academy: Strategy, Struggle, Survival." *Feminisms and Critical Pedagogy.* Eds. Carmen Luke and Jennifer Gore. New York: Routledge, 1992. 192–210.

Lutz, Catherine, and Jane Collins. *Reading National Geographic.* Chicago: University of Chicago Press, 1993.

Lyotard, Jean-Francois. *The Postmodern Condition: A Report on Knowledge.* Trans. Geoff Bennington and Brian Jameson. Minneapolis: University of Minnesota Press, 1993. Trans. Of *La Condition postmoderne: Rapport sur le savoir.* 1979.

Makaryk, Irena, ed. *Encyclopedia of Contemporary Literary Theory: Approaches, Scholars, Terms.* Toronto, ON: University of Toronto Press, 1993.

Martin, Carol, ed. *Local Colour.* Toronto, ON: Douglas & McIntyre, 1994.

Massey, Doreen. "Power-Geometry and a Progressive Sense of Place." *Mapping the Futures: Local 'Cultures, Global Change.* Eds. Jon Bird, Barry Curtis, Tim Putnam, George Robertson, and Lisa Tickner. New York: Routledge, 1993. 59–69.

_____. *Space, Place, and Gender.* Minneapolis: University of Minnesota Press, 1994.

Maxim, George. *Social Studies and the Elementary School Child.* 6th ed. Upper Saddle River, NJ: Prentice-Hall, 1999.

Michaels, Anne. "Cleopatra's Love." *Poetry and Knowing: Speculative Essays and Interviews.* Ed. Tim Lilburn. Kingston, ON: Quarry Press, 1995. 177–183.

Milne, Courtney. *Spirit of the Land: Sacred Places in Native North America.* Toronto, ON: Penguin, 1994.

Minh-ha, Trinh T. "Writing Postcoloniality and Feminism." *The Post-Colonial Studies Reader.* Eds. Bill Ashcroft, Gareth Griffiths, and Helen Tiffin. New York: Routledge, 1995. 264–268.

Monmonier, Mark. *Drawing the Line: Tales of Maps and Cartocontroversy.* New York: Henry Holt and Company, 1995.

_____. *How to Lie with Maps.* 2nd ed. Chicago, IL: The University of Chicago Press, 1996.

Moore, Thomas. *The Re-enchantment of Everyday Life.* New York: HarperCollins, 1996.

Nash, Catherine. "Remapping the Body/Land: New Cartographies of Identity, Gender, and Landscape in Ireland." *Writing Women and Space: Colonial and Postcolonial Geographies.* Eds. Allison Blunt and Gillian Rose. New York: Guilford Press, 1994. 227–250.

New, Bill. *Science Lessons.* Lantzville, BC: Oolichan Books, 1996.

Noddings, Nel. "Social Studies and Feminism." *Theory and Research in Social Education* 20.3 (1992): 230–241.

Phelan, Peggy. *Unmarked: The Politics of Performance.* London: Routledge, 1993.

Pinar, William, William Reynolds, Patrick Slattery, and Peter Taubman. *Understanding Curriculum.* New York: Peter Lang, 1995.

Pinder, David. "Subverting Cartography: The Situationists and Maps of the City." *Environment and Planning A* 28 (1996): 405–427.

Pollock, Della. "Performing Writing." *The Ends of Performance.* Eds. Peggy Phelan and Jill Lane. New York: New York University Press, 1998. 73–103.

Pred, Allan. "Re-Presenting the Extended Present Moment of Danger: A Meditation on Hypermodernity, Identity, and the Montage Form." *Space and Social Theory.* Eds. Georges Benko and Ulf Strohmayer. Oxford, UK: Blackwell, 1997. 117–140.

Rabasa, José. "Allegories of Atlas." *The Post-Colonial Studies Reader.* Eds. Bill Ashcroft, Gareth Griffiths, and Helen Tiffin. New York: Routledge, 1995. 358–364.

Rich, Adrienne. *An Atlas of the Difficult World: Poems 1988–1991.* New York: W.W. Norton & Company, 1991.

Richardson, Laurel. "The Poetic Representation of Lives: Writing a Postmodern Sociology." *Studies in Symbolic Interaction* 13 (1992): 19–27.

Rook, Constance, ed. *Writing Home.* Toronto, ON: McClelland & Stewart, 1997.

Rose, Gillian. *Feminism and Geography: The Limits of Geographical Knowledge.* Minneapolis: University of Minnesota Press, 1993.

_____. "Progress in Geography and Gender. Or Something Else." *Progress in Human Geography* 17.4 (1993): 531–537.

Saskatchewan. Saskatchewan Education, Training and Employment. *Social Studies: A Curriculum Guide and Activity Guide for the Elementary Level.* Regina, SK. 1995.

de Saussure, Ferdinand. *Course in General Linguistics.* Trans. Roy Harris. Peru, IL: Open Court, 1983. Trans. of *Cours de linguistique générale.* 1972.

Shields, R. "Fancy Footwork: Walter Benjamin's Notes on Flânerie." *The Flâneur.* Ed. K. Tester. London: Routledge, 1994. 61–80.

Silverman, Kaja. *The Subject of Semiotics*. New York: Oxford University Press, 1983.

Sirotnik, Kenneth. "Society, Schooling, Teaching, and Preparing to Teach." *The Moral Dimensions of Teaching*. Eds. John Goodlad, Roger Soder and Kenneth Sirotnik. San Francisco: Jossey-Bass Publications, 1990. 296–325.

Slater, Frances, ed. *Language and Learning in the Teaching of Geography*. New York: Routledge, 1989.

Stoltman, Joseph. "Research on Geography Teaching." *Handbook of Research on Social Studies Teaching and Learning*. Ed. James Shaver. New York: Macmillan, 1991. 437–447.

Strong-Boag, Veronica. "No Longer Dull: The Feminist Renewal of Canadian History." *Canadian Social Studies* 32.2 (1998): 55–57.

Threadgold, Terry. *Feminist Poetics: Poiesis, Performance, Histories*. New York: Routledge, 1997.

Turnbull, David. *Maps Are Territories: Science Is an Atlas*. Chicago: University of Chicago Press, 1989.

Wood, Denis, and John Fels. "Designs on Signs/Myth and Meaning in Maps." *Cartographica* 23.3 (1986): 54–103.

Wright, Ian. *Elementary Social Studies: A Practical Approach*. 4th ed. Toronto, ON: Nelson Canada, 1995.

About the Author

Photo by Don Hall.

Wanda Hurren is Assistant Professor of Curriculum in the Faculty of Education at the University of Regina, Canada. She received her Ph.D. in curriculum and instruction from the University of British Columbia, Canada. Her research and teaching interests are in curriculum theory, textual practices, and embodied knowing. Her poetry and articles have been published in several literary and professional journals.

Studies in the Postmodern Theory of Education

General Editors
Joe L. Kincheloe & Shirley R. Steinberg

Counterpoints publishes the most compelling and imaginative books being written in education today. Grounded on the theoretical advances in criticalism, feminism, and postmodernism in the last two decades of the twentieth century, Counterpoints engages the meaning of these innovations in various forms of educational expression. Committed to the proposition that theoretical literature should be accessible to a variety of audiences, the series insists that its authors avoid esoteric and jargonistic languages that transform educational scholarship into an elite discourse for the initiated. Scholarly work matters only to the degree it affects consciousness and practice at multiple sites. Counterpoints' editorial policy is based on these principles and the ability of scholars to break new ground, to open new conversations, to go where educators have never gone before.

For additional information about this series or for the submission of manuscripts, please contact:

Joe L. Kincheloe & Shirley R. Steinberg
637 West Foster Avenue
State College, PA 16801

To order other books in this series, please contact our Customer Service Department:

(800) 770-LANG (within the U.S.)
(212) 647-7706 (outside the U.S.)
(212) 647-7707 FAX

Or browse online by series:

www.peterlang.com